Penzance

SURROUNDED by dramatic cliffs, rocky coves and sandy beaches, Penzance, the most westerly of Cornwall's major towns, lies only ten miles from Land's End. Its name means "holy headland", from the Cornish *pen* and *sans*, after the ancient chapel which once stood close to the site of the present church.

The path to prominence began in 1663 when Charles II made Penzance a new coinage town for the tin industry, and as maritime trade developed the town became increasingly prosperous.

Maria Branwell, mother of Charlotte, Emily and Anne Brontë, was born here, but Penzance's most famous son is perhaps Sir Humphrey Davy, one of the most influential scientists of his day and inventor of the Davy lamp, which saved many lives.

Today, the town and its surrounding area remain a source of inspiration for artists, writers and poets.

Contents

Complete Stories

Dear Readers...

WELCOME to "The People's Friend" Annual 2013! It's packed with twenty-five brand-new stories from your favourite authors, and you can enjoy a scenic trip round Britain with J. Campbell Kerr. There's a wonderful selection of poetry, as always, and our "Animal Acts" series takes a look at some talented creatures who delighted us as stars of the silver screen.

So relax and enjoy the great reading on offer – and remember, you can find a feast of fiction every week in "The People's Friend", available from your newsagent!

Your Editor

Poetry

p14

p29

J. Campbell Kerr Paintings

p151

Animal Acts

5

A Magical Time Of The Year

by Alana Duffy.

O H, it's awful," Karen said as she held up the small greetings card and stared at the fairy that she had drawn. Rather than the beautiful, magical creature she had hoped to create, staring back at her was a circus clown in a frilly blue dress with uneven wings.

It had been her daughter Lisa's idea to create personalised fairy cards for the children, which would accompany all their Christmas fairy cakes. Although it was a last-minute decision, it was a wonderful idea. The only drawback was that both Karen and Lisa were hopeless when it came to art and, with Christmas approaching, they needed the cards fast.

Lisa glanced over Karen's shoulder and giggled.

"Well, you've definitely improved, Mum," she teased. "Your last fairy looked more like a giant fly in a pink ballerina dress."

"Very funny." Karen playfully nudged her daughter's arm. Just then, the shop door opened and a gust of cold wind whirled around the warm shop. A man dressed in a Santa Claus outfit, with a black satchel draped over his shoulder, strode toward the counter. His face was partially covered by a fake white beard and short tufts of wispy brown hair stuck out of the Santa hat.

Lisa suppressed a giggle as Karen said, "I hate to tell you this, Santa, but I'm afraid you're early. Christmas Eve isn't for another two weeks yet."

The man's warm hazel eyes crinkled as he smiled behind his beard.

"I'm afraid I'm not the real Santa," he said. "He's still in the North Pole. I was just roped in to playing the rôle for my granddaughter's school Christmas party this afternoon, only I left my normal clothes at home."

"I see." Karen smiled as Lisa disappeared into the back room.

"Apparently, I had the right build, tone and gentleness to make a convincing Santa," he continued. "That, and there was no-one else available."

Karen laughed.

"Well, you almost had me fooled," she said. "My name is Karen Sweet."

"John Baxter." He smiled and gently shook her hand.

"Well, John, what can I get for you today?"

"I'm not quite sure." His eyebrows knitted together as he admired the wide selection of delicacies lined up along the counter. "I have an art class in a few hours at Hanks Leisure Centre, so I need something quick and simple that I can heat up, but nothing too heavy. What would you recommend?"

7

His gaze held hers for a moment and she felt herself blush.

"Well, we have some delicious mini steak and kidney pies, and for dessert you could try our new Christmas muffins." Karen held out a small muffin, perfectly decorated with white chocolate swirls and topped with little holly leaves made from green icing. "Even a pretend Santa needs a treat after a hard day's work delivering presents to excited children."

As John laughed and reached across the counter to take the cake, his fingers lightly brushed hers and she felt her body tingle.

"This looks delicious. Did you make this yourself?"

Karen nodded.

"My daughter, Lisa, and I make all the cakes, pastries and pies."

"Well, I have to say these all look delightful," he said as Lisa walked back behind the counter carrying a tray of freshly made chocolate chip cookies. "My wife used to make some wonderful dishes. When she passed away I discovered how hopeless I was in the kitchen. Somehow I even manage to burn beans on toast." He grinned.

Suddenly his attention was drawn to the fairy greetings card, which was now lying on the counter. A smile danced across his lips.

"MY granddaughter creates little works of art like that, too," he said as he tilted his head and surveyed the picture more closely. "Erm . . . what is it, exactly?"

Karen felt her cheeks flush as Lisa spoke.

"This is my mum's interpretation of a fairy."

John's eyes widened.

"You mean you . . . Oh dear," he said, embarrassed with himself. "I'm terribly sorry, Karen. I didn't mean to offend you."

Karen laughed and held her hand up to interrupt him.

"You haven't offended me, John. I know it's pretty awful," she said.

"I've told you, Mum, we should just hire someone to make the cards for us. It would make life a lot easier," Lisa said. "I've already spoken to someone from BPL printers and they can create designs then print the greetings cards in batch numbers. The fee is quite reasonable. Mr Powell is going to pop round within the next day or two with some samples for us to look at."

Seeing Karen's reluctance, Lisa's face softened.

"I know you were hoping to create the cards yourself, but there's no harm in looking at the designs."

"Anyone can draw, Karen, you just have to have the right teacher," John said. "Why don't you come to the art lesson tonight? It'll be a very relaxed atmosphere and I know the teacher well; he's patient, caring and eager to guide all his students to their full potential."

"I'm not sure," she said nervously. "I'm not very good – as you've already seen. I don't want to embarrass myself in front of everyone."

John shook his head.

"The class ranges in age and ability, so you won't feel like the odd one out, and the first introductory lesson is free." He gave her a reassuring smile. "You won't be alone. I'll be there to look after you."

A FEW hours later, Karen stepped into the crowded classroom and gazed at the rows of easels, pots of paints and the group of people who mingled with each other. It did seem very relaxed, but that didn't stop her stomach from knotting with nerves.

"Come on, Karen. You can do this," she told herself firmly. Suddenly the door opened and John strolled in, dressed in casual black trousers and a blue striped shirt. He walked towards his desk at the front of the room and turned to the class, which had now fallen silent.

"Good evening, folks." His deep voice echoed around the room. "Welcome to your third art lesson."

After his introductory speech, John set everyone the task of drawing a single apple, which he had placed on a small table at the front of the class. Then he strolled around the room, observing and advising his students whenever necessary. When he approached Karen, his hazel eyes lit up.

"Hello, Karen Sweet." A smile danced across his lips. "I was hoping you'd come tonight. How are you getting on?"

"Not very well," she mumbled and gestured towards the circular object she had drawn that more resembled a misshapen ball of clay than it did an apple.

John's face softened.

"Don't worry, even the greatest of artists have to start somewhere."

He stepped closer and glanced at her drawing. Then, taking her hand, he gently guided the pencil around the paper, creating a perfect circle.

"The trick is not to be afraid, let the pencil run effortlessly across the paper."

Karen couldn't help admiring his confidence and gentleness when guiding his students into the perfect pencil strokes and correct shadings. And she couldn't ignore the flutter in her stomach whenever he glanced towards her.

* * * *

Before she realised it, the hour was over and all the students were heading out of the hall, chatting happily amongst themselves.

"So how did you find your first art lesson?" John said as he approached her easel. "Not too traumatic, I hope."

Karen smiled.

"You were right; it was a very relaxed and enjoyable evening. Although, I'm not too sure about the teacher," she teased. "He seems a real stickler for perfection."

John laughed.

"Oh, dear, maybe we should stick pins on his seat or ants in his drawer – that should liven up the lessons."

Karen laughed, too. She was surprised at how easily she relaxed in his company. She hadn't felt so comfortable with anyone since her husband, George, passed away a few years ago.

"So can I tempt you with another lesson?"

"I'm afraid not. I enjoyed tonight, but I don't think I have the talent to create the designs I was hoping for," she said. "And with Christmas in a few weeks I think it's best that I see what designs Mr Powell has to offer."

John's smile faded and he gazed down at his feet.

"I have a confession to make, Karen. There is no Mr Powell," he said. "It's Mrs Kate Powell . . . my daughter."

Karen frowned.

"I don't understand."

"I'm John Baxter of BPL – Baxter Powell Limited. My daughter runs the company, while I draw and create the designs. I came into your shop today not only to purchase one of your home-made pies – which were delicious, by the way," he added. "But I had also brought some designs to show you."

Karen watched as he walked towards his desk, took his satchel and retrieved an envelope from inside.

Carefully, Karen opened it and pulled out the enclosed note. Around the edges of the crisp white greetings card was the most exquisite decoration she had ever seen. The swirling patterns were embellished in gold and silver glitter, outlined by thick black ink. In the right-hand corner of the card was a small and delicately drawn fairy with long wavy red hair, the wings and blue flowing dress sparkling with silver glitter in the moonlight.

"This is beautiful!" she said. "Just how I envisaged the cards. Why didn't you tell me who you were before? Why did you invite me to this class?"

John smiled.

"I could see how much you wanted to create your own greetings cards and I thought the art class might help. And I was hoping to see you again."

"Oh." Karen grinned. "Well, I'm glad I came tonight, and your design is perfect." She was thoughtful for a moment before she said, "I don't suppose you would consider helping me with the Christmas greetings cards? You could create the designs and I could add a personal message to each of them."

John's eyes lit up as his smile widened.

"I'd love to help you, Karen," he said. "Perhaps we could seal the deal over a pre-Christmas drink? There's a nice little pub just across the road with a roaring fire."

They stepped out into the night and strolled towards the White Dove Inn, just as the newly formed snowflakes began to fall. Despite the cold, Karen felt warm inside. She had always believed Christmas was a magical time of year. ■

10

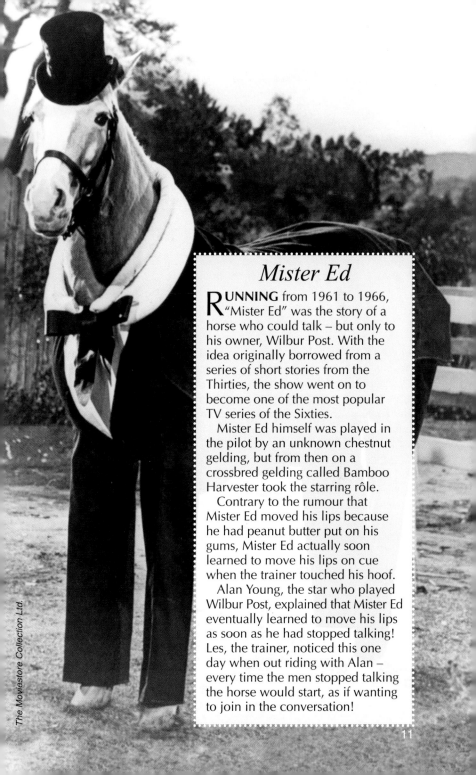

Mister Ed

RUNNING from 1961 to 1966, "Mister Ed" was the story of a horse who could talk – but only to his owner, Wilbur Post. With the idea originally borrowed from a series of short stories from the Thirties, the show went on to become one of the most popular TV series of the Sixties.

Mister Ed himself was played in the pilot by an unknown chestnut gelding, but from then on a crossbred gelding called Bamboo Harvester took the starring rôle.

Contrary to the rumour that Mister Ed moved his lips because he had peanut butter put on his gums, Mister Ed actually soon learned to move his lips on cue when the trainer touched his hoof.

Alan Young, the star who played Wilbur Post, explained that Mister Ed eventually learned to move his lips as soon as he had stopped talking! Les, the trainer, noticed this one day when out riding with Alan – every time the men stopped talking the horse would start, as if wanting to join in the conversation!

Making The Effort

by Suzanne Jones.

DOUGLAS handed over his money and picked up a newspaper and a chocolate bar, as he did every morning on his way to work. "You'll be going to the party tonight." Rose McLeod's pale blue eyes were bright. "It's all my customers have been talking about for days."

He could think of nothing worse than being in a social situation, forced to try to talk when he couldn't think of anything to say.

"I don't think so."

She sighed as she handed him his change.

"You should go. It's difficult moving to a new town in winter – everyone tends to hurry indoors to keep warm. This will be a chance for you to meet people."

It was true he had yet to make friends here. But he'd only moved six weeks ago and he'd never found it easy to talk to new people.

"It's not really my kind of thing. Will you be there?"

"Ah, no, that's not for me – not these days." She straightened a pile of magazines on the cluttered counter. "I'll be cosy upstairs in my flat. I might stay up for the bells, but my times for dancing until dawn are long gone."

He wanted to say something encouraging to make her reconsider, but was at a loss. He was always like that around new people – awkward. Hours later the perfect response would appear unbidden on his tongue, but always when it was too late.

He folded his newspaper and put his chocolate in his pocket.

"I'll see you next year." Rose laughed softly, although he was sure she'd have made the same joke to all her customers today.

He smiled and turned to leave the tiny shop – crashing into the giant Christmas tree on his way.

That was the thing with being large-framed, you needed a lot of room to manoeuvre.

"Sorry," he muttered, embarrassed, as he tried to straighten the ornaments he'd dislodged.

"No need to be sorry, love. The tree's far too big for the shop, but I can never resist. I like the way it can be seen from the street on these dark days.

And I know I shouldn't, but I always leave the lights on overnight, too. Cheers everyone up, they tell me."

As Douglas walked the short distance to work, he worried that he should have said something about it being kind, sharing the Christmas tree. Because it was.

Rose was relentlessly cheerful and always had a kind word for him. In fact, she was the closest thing he had to a friend in this town. He should have made a bigger effort.

He thought briefly about the place he'd left behind, and he missed the people he'd known for ever. He'd been able to talk to them easily. But jobs were hard to come by these days and he was lucky to have found work, even if it meant moving two hundred miles south.

* * * *

The building was nearly deserted when he arrived, most of the employees having chosen to take annual leave to extend their break. He liked it when it was quiet: much easier to get on with things. That was one of the reasons

13

he'd volunteered to cover the department over the festive period. And, even though he'd considered going home, both his colleagues had young families, so it seemed only fair.

He'd only been at his desk for five minutes when his phone rang.

"IT department, Douglas speaking."

"Oh, hi." A breathless voice came from the other end. "I'm so glad you're there. I wasn't sure anyone would be in – I mean, everyone else seems to be on holiday . . ."

Douglas frowned. He could guess what was coming. People were only ever glad he was here when there was a problem.

"How can I help you?"

"This is Sheena, from the executive floor. My computer's decided not to work today and I'm desperately trying to get an urgent report finished, so it's a bit of a disaster."

Douglas wondered what could be so urgent on New Year's Eve when it was very probable that, apart

Once Upon A Time

Thinkstockphotos.

from security staff, only he and Sheena were in the building. But he thought it would be rude to ask.

"Can you tell me exactly what's happened?"

He listened carefully as Sheena explained.

"I've tried restarting it." She sounded almost apologetic now and Douglas rushed to reassure her.

"I'll be there in a minute." He had a pretty good idea what was wrong and how to fix it and, if he was right, it wouldn't take long. He'd be back in the safety of his own department before he knew it.

She bounded over to meet him as the lift doors opened.

"I really appreciate this."

"No problem."

He'd seen her before, he realised, in the staff canteen at lunchtime. She was small and pretty and always seemed to be chatting to someone.

"I can't tell you how grateful I am to see you. All my data's on this PC and

THE house asleep like a blue ship
  under deep water;
The moon piercing the skylight
  window.
I padded down, bare feet trying not
  to creak the stairs
Out under the jewellery of the stars.

The hushed bark of a dog,
The last pears fallen from the tree
  in red-gold slush,
The moon cast over the garden,
  such bright shadow;
I could have wandered miles
  and miles.

And that was what I longed for –
To lose myself in the story of
  the forest,
Come out in some magical tale
Written by wolves and snow.

— *Kenneth Steven.*

I really need to get this finished."

Douglas made a start on solving the problem while Sheena continued to chat.

"The board are meeting early in the New Year and they need this report by this afternoon so they can prepare. I promised I could do it and they'll be furious if the figures aren't ready for them. Thank you so much, I'm very grateful."

She finally paused for breath and he searched for the right words. He didn't find them. But at least he now knew why Sheena was at work, rather than spending the day preparing for the town's New Year party, like everyone else.

"No need to be grateful," he said at last. "I'm just doing my job."

He was aware of her fluttering nervously as he worked. She really was concerned about this report. He wished there was something he could say to calm her down. Just as well he knew computers better than he knew human beings.

"Are you going to the party tonight, Douglas?"

His impressions of Sheena had been spot on – it seemed she liked to talk. Just a pity he was the least chatty man she was likely to encounter.

He glanced around. Her eyes were bright and he could see she was obviously very much looking forward to the event.

"I don't think so."

"Oh? Why not?"

"Not my kind of thing."

He wondered if he should have those words printed on his forehead – to save everyone the bother of asking. Despite himself, he smiled at her look of utter shock.

"But everyone's going. You'll have a great time. What are you doing instead?"

"I thought I'd have an early night."

"We're planning very loud music – we'll wake you up." She giggled. "Really, you should pop by, even for a short while. You can always leave if you hate it."

"I'll think about it," Douglas muttered, although he had no intention of doing any such thing.

"There you go." He stood up and stepped away from Sheena's desk. "Problem solved."

"Oh, thank you. That's great – and such a relief."

She stood on tiptoe and surprised him by pecking him on the cheek. In fact, she looked a bit surprised herself, but quickly recovered and smiled.

"You're my hero."

His face became suddenly warm and the floral scent of her perfume tickled his nose. Douglas couldn't get out of there fast enough. Nobody had ever called him a hero before. He wasn't comfortable with it.

"Hopefully see you later," she called at his retreating back.

* * * *

Sheena had been nice, he realised as he arrived back at his desk. He should have tried harder to speak to her.

The more he thought about her insistence he should go to the party, the more he was tempted. He couldn't forget the softness of her lips on his cheek or the scent of her perfume as she'd leaned in close.

He knew she wouldn't have meant anything by it – kissing was what people did on New Year's Eve. But, if he was going to try to make friends in this new place, he could do worse than start with her.

Besides, he knew it was daft for a man his age to be so shy around people he didn't know. He had lots of friends in his home town and had plenty to say to them, so he should make an effort not to be so awkward around new people.

By the time he left work, he'd talked himself into going to the party and he rushed home to get changed. But he realised he was out of his depth as soon as he arrived. The hall was bursting at the seams – Rose McLeod had not been joking when she'd said everyone would be there.

He scanned the place and spotted Sheena at the other side of the room. They made eye contact and she smiled and waved, but Douglas couldn't bring himself to go over – not when she was surrounded by her friends.

It was hard not to be pulled along by the jolly atmosphere, though, and he quickly found himself involved in a conversation about the band that were playing. Time rushed by and he was surprised to find he'd quite enjoyed himself, but as midnight approached he decided it might be an idea to make himself scarce. The thought of being required to kiss strangers was just a step too far.

Once again, he found himself thinking of Sheena and how he wouldn't object to kissing her. But he hadn't been able to get close to her all night. However much he might want to, he never quite found the courage to brave the crowd permanently surrounding her.

With a sigh, he slipped out into the night, just before midnight. He could hear the countdown from inside and smiled. Then the cries of "Happy New Year" reached him and he knew they would be kissing and hugging everyone in sight.

He walked away to the strains of "Auld Lang Syne".

THE sky was clear and the air was exactly as cold as anyone would expect it to be so early on a January morning.

He spent some time wandering around the town before making his way home, enjoying the solitude, although he wished he'd been brave enough to stay and make his way to Sheena's side at midnight.

The twinkling lights of Rose McLeod's Christmas tree were visible from outside the shop, just as she'd said they would be. He stopped to admire them for a moment. But, as he watched, he realised the lights weren't twinkling as much as flickering. And the light was burning orange. The shop was on fire.

"Rose!" he shouted, as he banged on the door. "Rose, are you in there?"

He knew she had to be, she'd told him she was staying home – and there had been no sign of her at the party.

His hands were shaking as he quickly fished his mobile from his pocket and dialled the emergency services. And then, heart pounding, he shouldered the door.

It gave instantly and he reeled back as the heat hit him. But he forced his way through and made his way up the staircase leading to the flat above the shop.

Thankfully, the fire hadn't reached the living-room where Rose still sat in her chair, but the air was thick with smoke. Rose didn't respond to his shouts, so he lifted her easily into his arms and headed for the door.

He couldn't remember afterwards how he got her out of there, but he did recall there had been a point where he'd been unsure they'd make it out of the building. By the time he staggered on to the street, the fire engine and ambulance had arrived.

Rose still wasn't conscious, but she was breathing and he handed her gently over to the paramedics. He felt suddenly weak and stood back to lean against a wall. He supposed a rush of adrenalin would do that to a person.

People were arriving now, summoned by the sirens and curious to know what was going on.

"What's happening?" someone shouted.

"It's Rose," another cried.

"Is she OK?"

Douglas took advantage of the flurry of activity and slipped away. He'd ring the hospital later to make sure Rose was OK. Hanging around now wasn't going to achieve anything. But he desperately needed to go home and clean up – the stench of the fire clung to him like a second skin.

He was only just out of the shower when the doorbell rang. First-footers, he supposed. He hurriedly threw on some clean clothes and arrived at the door as the bell was rung for the second time.

"Sheena? Is that you?"

The last person he'd expected to see on his doorstep.

"Hi." She smiled and followed him into the living-room, where she sat on the sofa. "Everyone's looking for you."

"Why?"

She looked startled.

"To make sure you're OK. We're all worried."

"I'm fine," he replied, embarrassment making his voice gruff. He didn't want a fuss.

"And everyone wants to congratulate the hero of the hour. Thanks to you, they think Rose will make a full recovery. But if you hadn't passed by when you did . . ."

"Anybody would have done the same."

She shook her head.

"Everyone else was busy enjoying themselves. They think the fire started with the tree. She's been told for years she shouldn't leave the lights on overnight."

"Rose was being kind. She wanted to cheer everyone up."

Sheena nodded.

"I know. She's always so nice, that's why she's loved by everyone in this town. The party isn't quite a party any longer, but everyone's still at the hall. They need to thank you."

"I don't know . . ."

"Look, I know you're shy, it's obvious to anyone. But you have to fight against it – give us a chance. We're nice people. Get to know us and you'll like us."

Douglas knew she meant well, but he didn't think she understood just how difficult it was for him.

"What would you know about being shy?"

She smiled.

"Why do you think I talk so much? Over-compensating for the fact it would be much easier for me to curl up quietly at home. But do you know something? The more I talk, the easier it gets. Please come back with me."

Douglas thought about the friends he'd left behind and how easy it had been to talk to them and he knew Sheena was speaking the truth. He needed to make an effort and that could start now.

Besides, he still remembered the feel of Sheena's lips against his cheek and he knew that he wouldn't be able to refuse her anything.

"OK," he agreed and got to his feet. "Let's go."

"Good. And one more thing . . ." She walked over and, for the second time in two days, brushed her lips against his cheek. "Happy New Year."

He smiled. Maybe he'd started this year on his own, but he very much hoped he would be ending it in her company.

"Happy New Year, Sheena." ■

Snowdrops For Remembrance

I **THINK** this year the snowdrops are more beautiful than ever. Or maybe they just seem that way because I didn't come to see them last year. Spring has arrived early and vast swathes of them carpet the valley floor, their fragile white flowers fully open in the warm February sun, trembling on slender green stems in the playful breeze.

I stoop and gently lift the head of one of the blooms so that I can see inside the white petals to the delicate, apple-green tinted frills within. So beautiful. For a moment my throat closes as memories threaten to overwhelm me.

I let the flower return its gaze to the ground and continue my leisurely stroll, following the leaf-strewn path through the trees that clothe the steep slopes of the isolated valley. A few feet below me, the river rushes over its stone bed, fast and foaming after the recent rain on the hills.

I take off my hat and lift my face to feel the slight warmth of the sun and the ruffling of the wind in my hair.

The path bears downhill to cross the river and I pause to lean on the rail of the wooden footbridge that spans the water. It seems strange to be here on my own. The children offered to come with me but I said no. This is something I have to do alone. I hope they understand that I need this to be a private

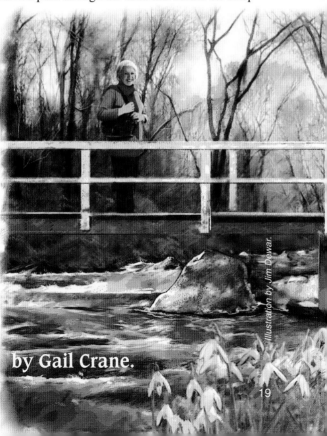

Illustration by Jim Dewar.

by Gail Crane.

moment for just the two of us.

I look at my watch. It shouldn't be long now. I want to make sure it is done before the crowds arrive.

The movement of the water beneath the bridge is almost hypnotic. I have nothing to do but wait – and think about that first time, now so long ago.

* * * *

The minibus pulled into the side of the road just as I reached the narrow entrance to the valley and I found myself caught up in the crowd as the passengers clambered out on to the muddy ground.

I guessed from their ages that it was probably an outing from an old people's home and some were decidedly shaky on their feet. I managed to negotiate my way round them and was about to stride off to explore the valley when there was a shout behind me and I turned to see one of the men fall heavily to the ground as his walking-stick slipped from under him in the mud.

I flew back and bent down beside him. He was shaken but assured me that he wasn't injured, and I was breathing a sigh of relief and wondering what to do next when someone came up behind me.

"Shall we try to help him over to that wall?" he suggested, crouching down on the other side of the man. "It's low enough for him to sit on until we can find something better."

As there didn't appear to be any other form of seating available, I agreed, and between us we made him comfortable until a harassed attendant rushed forward with a folding wheelchair.

"Thank you so much," she said as we helped her make the transfer. "This is turning out to be one of those days."

Having made sure there was nothing more we could do, my fellow helper and I moved off to see the snowdrops.

It happened quite naturally that we fell into step and began chatting. We covered the usual stuff about the weather and how lovely the scenery was and then he stopped and said, "I suppose we ought to introduce ourselves. I'm Don."

"I'm Margaret," I replied.

Then, nodding towards the serious-looking bit of kit hanging round his neck, I asked if he was a photographer.

He grimaced.

"That's the general plan, although so far I'm having difficulty convincing an employer of that. I do a bit of freelance work for the local rag, but I've only been out of college for a couple of years so I've a long way to go yet. What about you?"

"I'm studying horticulture. This is my final year."

It was amazing how easy he was to talk to and how well we got on together. By the time we'd completed the circuit of the valley it felt as though we were old friends, so when he invited me to go for lunch with him at the pub I said I would love to.

And that's how it all began.

THE following year we decided to mark the anniversary of our meeting by going back to the valley.

By now Don was working for a fashion magazine as a photographer's assistant, which really meant – as he put it – being a general dog's-body. But it was a step on the ladder, if only a small one, and I was thrilled for him.

I had passed my exams and found a wonderful job as a junior gardener at our local stately home, which meant I could spend my days in the fresh air with soil under my fingernails and the scents of plants and earth all around me. Bliss.

Spring was late and we were both wrapped up against the cold east wind that scoured the valley, buffeting the snowdrops that stood defiantly with their heads down and their buds tightly closed.

We were the only people brave, or daft, enough to be out and we had the valley to ourselves.

Don put his arm round my shoulders and pulled me towards him.

"Warm enough?" he asked.

"Mmm, just about," I said, snuggling closer.

He took off his glove and stroked my cold cheek.

"I love you," he murmured.

I opened my mouth to say I loved him, too, but before I could speak he dropped his head and our lips met, and there was no need for me to say anything because it was all there in that kiss.

When he stopped long enough to ask me to marry him, I said, "Oh, yes," and pulled his head down again to mine just to make absolutely sure that he understood.

*   *   *   *

I tightened my hold on Harry's hand as I walked slowly along the river path with him toddling along beside me on his sturdy three-year-old legs. The sloping bank was slippery with mud and Harry was too adventurous for his own good. If I didn't watch him he would be off to explore the river, completely oblivious of any danger he might be in.

Don dawdled in front of us, matching his long strides to Harry's short ones, carrying the peacefully sleeping Bella in a sling across his chest.

We were a bit later than usual coming here this year and the snowdrops were in full bloom. Don had been promoted and was now taking on assignments on his own – even, occasionally, with his own dog's-body to help him, something I teased him about mercilessly. Well, I couldn't let him get too above himself! But he laughed and took it all in good part.

My job hadn't changed, but then I'd had to make adjustments for two children and had only been able to work part-time since Harry's birth. I didn't mind. I was perfectly happy and there would always be time for me when the children were grown up.

Harry tugged at my hand and pulled me towards a clump of snowdrops so that he could have a closer look.

"Be careful," I told him. "We don't want to hurt the flower, do we?"

He placed one chubby little hand beneath a flowerhead and gently lifted it so that he could see inside, then he turned to me with a smile.

"Pretty," he said.

"Very pretty," I agreed.

I showed him how some of the snowdrops had different patterns and after that we had to stop at every new clump so that he could tip up the flower and look inside.

Eventually, he grew tired of this game and I picked him up and piggy-backed him the rest of the way.

The sun was going down behind the hill by the time we got back to the car and the children were asleep almost before Don had strapped them into their car seats. We stood for a few minutes side by side, leaning on the car, watching the shadows lengthen and the sky turn red.

Don turned towards me.

"Happy?" he asked.

I reached up and kissed his cheek.

"Very," I said.

* * * *

We almost didn't come this year but Don was insistent that he could manage and, as he said himself, this might be his last chance. But, for the first time, the beauty of the snowdrops failed to move us. We had weightier matters on our minds.

February

SHOULD morning mist descend
at dawn
Or fog greet us this very morn,
Just for a while the outlook's grey
But soon the sun will shine our way!

Then gradually the day turns bright,
And we're uplifted by the sight
Of a lone snowdrop, peeping through
The earth, as if to greet us, too!

– Joan Zambelli.

It had been quite a year all told, what with Bella's wedding and Harry going off to med school and Don having to spend so much time in and out of hospital.

We walked slowly, taking our time, until we reached the bridge across the river. There we paused to lean on the rail and watch the water beneath us. That's been our life, I thought, flowing inexorably forward, sometimes moving swiftly, unhampered, sometimes having to fight its way through the rocks that lay in its path.

Don put his arm round me and I leaned in to him, resting my head on his shoulder.

"Hard to believe that in a few months we'll be grandparents, isn't it?" I murmured.

His only answer was to pull me a little closer.

It was a cold February day and I shivered as the Arctic wind whipped round my legs and turned my face numb. I slipped my hand into Don's.

"Come on," I said. "Let's move."

We walked on in companionable silence, following the snowdrop-lined path, each deep in our own thoughts. Then Don broke the silence.

"Do you remember the first time we came here?" he said.

I smiled.

"How could I forget?"

"Remember the old man who fell in the mud?" He sighed. "You know, they really should provide seats for us oldies."

"I hope you're not suggesting I'm old?" I teased, laughing.

But I knew what he was thinking and I put my arms around him and hugged him, wishing that I could infuse into him some of my own health and energy.

Slowly, we made our way back to the gate and sat for a while on the wall to rest and I thought of all the times we had walked round the river path over the years, first just the two of us, then with the children until they grew up and left home to lead their own lives.

Now it was just the two of us again.

I leaned towards Don and whispered in his ear, "I love you."

* * * *

I shiver and realise I'm cold.

How long have I been standing here leaning over the bridge, watching the water flow beneath like a time-line of memories rushing past as though it was all yesterday?

I check my watch. I must make a move. I'm supposed to be meeting them at the gate in five minutes. It's just eighteen months now since Don died.

I didn't come last year because I couldn't bear the thought of being here without him. It was the children who persuaded me to come back, who told me that I should remember the good times we'd had here together, that I should come here and think of him. That was when the plan had begun to form in my mind.

Putting it into practice has given me something to concentrate on through the long days of missing him. I hope he approves.

But I've already spent too much time with my thoughts. I must hurry.

I'm just in time. The van pulls into the side of the road as I reach the gate. I wait while the men unload, then I lead them along the path to the place I have chosen. A place that catches the warmth of the sun. A place where the mossy, tree-covered slopes fall away in a profusion of snowdrops to the tumbling river below.

The men place the seat on the patch that has been prepared for it and I stand back to admire it. Perfect.

I wait until they've gone and I'm alone, then I sit down and run my hand over the smooth surface of the oak until it reaches the small brass plate on the back rest. It reads: *In memory of Don, who loved this place.*

I think Don would be pleased if he knew. Perhaps he does. Who knows? It was really his idea, after all.

People are arriving now and soon it will be crowded and I shall no longer have the valley to myself. I sit for a while longer, thinking and remembering. Shall I come back? I don't know. I've said my goodbyes.

I run my hand over the inscription once more and whisper a quiet farewell, then I stand up. I shall take one last stroll round the valley before I go.

As I walk away an elderly couple come and sit on the seat and I overhear one of them, with a sigh of relief, say how wonderful it is that someone has put a seat here at last.

I smile to myself. Yes, I think Don would be happy with that. And I know, in that moment, that I will come back. Maybe not next year or the one after, but one day I will bring my grandchildren here to see the snowdrops and we'll sit on the seat and I'll tell them all about the grandpa they will never know – and together we will remember. ■

Going Solo

THIS really was a beautiful hotel. Passing the ground floor function rooms, already decked out for the evening ahead, Fran made her way towards the sweeping staircase that would lead her upstairs to the special suite.

Giving a nod and a smile to her brother, Joe, who was home from uni for a few days and was already setting up a meet-and-greet table at the entrance, she stepped inside. Looking around at the pristine white linen tablecloths and the little vases of fresh flowers, she gave herself a mental pat on the back.

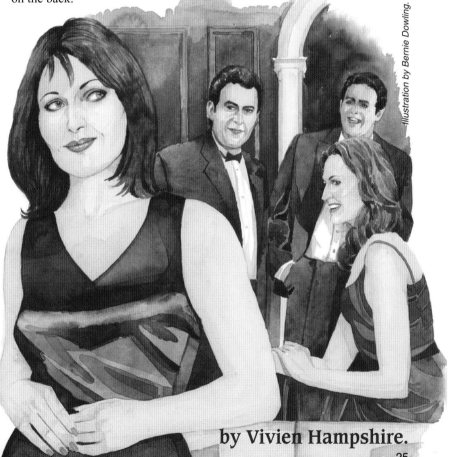

Illustration by Bernie Dowling.

by Vivien Hampshire.

Fran had never organised a social event on this scale before and she was still nervous about it. What if nobody turned up? What if the whole thing was a total flop and all the guests just ended up feeling depressed and more alone than ever? Quickly, she snapped herself out of it. Of course they would come – tickets had been selling like hot cakes.

The idea for a dinner party that flew in the face of convention, a special Valentine's Day celebration for those who not only had no Valentine of their own but didn't necessarily even want one, had started as a tiny germ of an idea just over two years ago. It was just after Greg had ended their relationship, very suddenly, after four years together.

One minute it had seemed they were sailing along in cosy coupledom, the next he was telling her he felt too young to be tied down and needed some freedom. Everything had come crashing down around her with a bump, Greg had flown off to America and a new job, and suddenly she was alone.

She had started the online blog as a way of letting off steam, issuing a weekly rant about the agonies of her newly single life. She didn't really care if anyone read it; just writing and sending it out there via the internet was cathartic enough. And, slowly, her heart had begun to heal . . . She was only twenty-six, after all, and staying at home with nothing but a cup of cocoa and a bag of knitting to look forward to did not really appeal.

She wasn't looking for romance. Far from it! Once bitten, twice shy, that was her motto now, but she was determined to get back out and enjoy life again, even if she had to do it alone.

The trouble was that the real world seemed geared very much towards couples. When she had been half of one herself, she hadn't noticed these things, but she did now. She was acutely aware of the supermarkets' dinner-for-two deals, hotels always charging a single supplement, buy-one-get-one-free tickets to the cinema.

AND that was when Going Solo was born. A website of her own, tracking down and spreading the news about the shops, holidays and hotels willing to offer the best deals to people on their own. It had seemed the next natural step from writing her blog, and it had been a rip-roaring, and totally unexpected, success.

Going Solo now had thousands of members right across the country, it had been featured on daytime TV, and companies were falling over themselves to offer deals and grab some advertising space on the website.

Fran closed her eyes and took a deep breath. Now some of those members were about to meet face-to-face for the very first time and she hoped it wasn't going to be a complete disaster.

"I'm not sure about these badges, Fran." Joe was standing beside her, wielding a box of name pins. "I mean, who wants to walk about with *Dapper* or *Bunny B* pinned to their chest?"

"But those are their user names! They're happy to call themselves by all manner of names when they chat online."

"Exactly. But this is real life, Fran. Real people don't introduce themselves by silly nicknames, or hide behind them. How will they get to know each other if they don't tell anyone who they really are?"

Fran had to concede that he had a point.

"I suppose so. But don't you go getting any ideas about this evening being an excuse to pair people off. I keep telling you that Going Solo is not a dating site! It may be Valentine's Day, but that's no reason for any of us to have to hide indoors or feel embarrassed just because we are on our own.

"I want to give members the chance to get dressed up in all their finery and eat a nice meal together at a posh hotel, without having to be in love with someone to be invited, or to enjoy themselves."

Joe said nothing. She watched him shaking his head as he went back to his place at the door and slipped the box of badges discreetly away in a corner. She sat down for a moment, enjoying the lull before the storm, and admired the grandeur of the room.

She had chosen large round dining-tables, where groups of ten or twelve could chat and eat together and forget all about what was happening tonight in every other restaurant in the land.

There wasn't a rose in sight – there was no need to parade the over-rated idea of romance in front of those who had chosen – or been forced – to live without it. Tonight, she was sure, wasn't just going to be different. It was going to be fun.

JOE could hear the sounds of the first guests arriving in the hotel lobby down below. As a group of hesitant-looking men and women wandered up the staircase one at a time towards him, he straightened his bow tie and prepared to smile, shake hands and take their tickets. That's what Fran was paying him to do tonight, after all, not to voice his opinions.

Much as he loved his big sister, and admired what she had achieved, he did feel a bit sorry for her.

Her constant anti-romance stance was just a show, he was certain. She'd been happy enough with the hearts and flowers when Greg had still been around. He wasn't sure if she was still feeling bitter, or if it was her rather strange way of denying what she really wanted.

"Good evening, and welcome to Going Solo's Getting Together Evening."

In spite of his sister's insistence that this was not a dating evening, Joe couldn't help hoping that at least some of them would not be leaving alone. He didn't like to say it out loud, but he was a bit of a romantic at heart.

The room was filling up fast now, the women in an array of formal dresses in bright colours, the men in their dinner suits and stiff white shirts. Some stood by themselves, looking either lost or scared, while others were making the effort to chat.

He could see Fran across the room, in her smart purple satin dress, moving around from group to group, introducing herself, pointing the way to the bar and ushering guests to tables. He couldn't help smiling to himself as he wondered which one of them might be Dapper or Bunny B.

"Good evening."

He pulled his attention back to the job he was here to do, and to the man waiting in front of him, and held out his hand to take his ticket.

"Joe? Joe, it is you, isn't it? I hardly recognised you without your usual jeans and crash helmet! You look quite grown-up in that suit. How have you been?" The man held out his hand, grabbed Joe's and shook it firmly.

"Greg? What on earth are you doing here? I thought you were still in America." Joe looked behind him furtively. "You're the last person Fran will want to see tonight."

"Fran? Oh, don't tell me she's here! She's not, is she?"

"Well, of course she is. This is her party – Going Solo is her website, her business venture. You must have known that."

The man looked sheepish.

"No. No, I didn't. I've not long been back in the country and I just saw the advert and thought it sounded a good idea for a single man like me, with nowhere better to go on Valentine's night. Perhaps I should just leave, slip away quietly before she spots me. What do you think?"

"I think you're too late." Joe shook his head and sighed. "She's already seen you, and she's on her way over."

FRAN could feel her heart pounding a lot faster than it had been just a moment before. She wanted to force a smile, ask how he was and walk away with dignity, but suddenly, as the sweat broke out on her palms and she had trouble walking in a straight line towards him, she knew she wasn't going to be able to do it.

Why tonight, of all nights? What was he doing here? All manner of thoughts battled their way into her head at once, but not one of them helped her to decide what to say. She reached the doorway.

"Greg . . ."

"Hello, Fran. You're looking very nice tonight." He hesitated. "Actually, you're looking fantastic!"

"Thanks," she muttered, trying hard to control the blush which was threatening to engulf her face.

Greg looked concerned.

"I'm really sorry if me being here causes a problem for you. I genuinely had no idea you would be here. I've been meaning to come and see you actually, ever since I got back, but I wasn't sure you'd want to see me. I'm a bit of a coward still, and I wasn't too sure of the reception I might get, to be

Dundee (*RRS Discovery*)

JAM, jute and journalism are the things most associated with this jewel of the "silvery Tay", but "Bonnie Dundee", as it was hailed by one of its most famous sons, poet William McGonagall, has long been a centre of exploration and innovation.

With its long experience of constructing whaling ships, Dundee was the first choice to build the *RRS Discovery*, the first ship to be built specifically to undertake scientific research. The joint Royal Society and Royal Geographical Society 1901-04 expedition to the Antarctic, commanded by Captain Robert Falcon Scott RN, was the source of important scientific, geological and zoological knowledge, and the restored ship is now a popular visitor attraction at the city's Discovery Quay.

Still at the forefront of developments in biomedical and digital technology (and the home of some famous computer games such as "Lemmings") the City of Discovery has a wealth of wonders just waiting to be explored!

honest. But fate seems to have stepped in."

"Yes."

Oh, why was she not able to say more than one word at a time? Where was the confident, independent business woman she was supposed to be? She swallowed hard and turned on her best smile. He was a guest, just like any other, and it was her job to make sure he felt comfortable and enjoyed the evening.

"But of course you being here isn't a problem, Greg. All members are welcome tonight. Very welcome and you are no exception. Where else could we singletons go without sticking out like a sore thumb?" She laughed quietly, nervously, and fought back the urge to turn and run. Was he still single? Who knew what might have happened since they'd last met?

"May I buy you a drink? For old times' sake. Still white wine, is it?" He stepped into the room, looked around for the bar, and started to steer her towards it.

"I'm working," Fran protested, very aware of the warmth of his hand against her bare elbow.

"Oh, I'm sure young Joe can manage without you for a while. That lad certainly has changed. What is he now? Nineteen? And how are your parents? Still hate me, I expect."

"They're fine, and they never hated you. Not even . . ."

"When I walked out on you?"

"Well, yes. But they were great, actually. A real support to me."

"I'm glad, Fran. And I'm sorry. After all this time, I'm still sorry. More than you can know."

He pushed a glass of wine towards her, and she felt her hand tremble as she took it. No, no, she couldn't let him see just how much he still had the power to affect her. She took a small sip and then quickly put the glass down on the nearest table.

"I have things to do, Greg, and other guests to attend to."

"Maybe later then? A chat? Just as friends . . ."

She nodded and moved away, too scared to look back. She concentrated on her breathing – deep breaths. This was her big night and she could not let anything spoil it.

YOU don't have to do that, Fran." Joe loosened his tie and slumped down into a comfy leather chair, as she tidied up stray glasses. "The last guests have gone and all we have to do is finish this wonderful champagne and go home."

He pulled her down next to him and tugged the two empty beer mugs out of her hands.

"It went really well, you know. Everyone enjoyed it. Come on, take a sip. Let's celebrate. You should be proud."

He slid the champagne in front of her, but she just shrugged.

"What's up, sis? Is it Greg?"

"Of course not!"

"I just thought maybe . . ."

"Maybe, what? He bought me a drink, Joe, and we had a short but civilised conversation and he even said he was sorry. But I still wanted to scream and throw something at him!"

She sighed and closed her eyes, leaning her head back against the cool wood panelling and running her hands hard through her hair, pushing it back from her forehead.

"You don't mean that."

NO, you're right, I don't. I'm just tired. In fact, I don't even feel angry with him any more. Perhaps he was right all along and we were too young. I had no career back then, no life plan beyond marriage and babies, and he just wanted to see the world. If we'd stayed together, we would have been holding each other back, and I would never have started Going Solo, that's for sure."

"And now?"

"I don't know what you mean. Look, he's gone, hasn't he? He didn't even say goodbye so I think that answers your question. And, before you think about saying what I know you want to say, no, I don't want another romance – and certainly not with Greg."

"If you're sure."

"Let's just change the subject, shall we?"

"Ah, I think the lady protests too much!"

She gave him a sisterly swipe, and got to her feet.

"Enough of your nonsense; it's time to go home!"

They found their coats and walked down the stairs. In the lobby, a few stray red balloons had floated down from the ceiling and were bobbing along the carpet, and a man and a woman were standing close.

"Ah, how sweet," Joe said. "See, Fran, two of your members getting to know each other. It may not be a dating website you're running, but you can't stand in the way of love when it comes knocking, no matter how hard you try. And that reminds me, I promised to call Lucy again before midnight, and I've only got five minutes to spare."

"It's late. Won't she be asleep?"

"No, she'll be waiting up to talk to me, just to say goodnight. It won't take long, I'll catch you up."

Fran walked as far as the big revolving doors that led to the street. It must be nice to have someone like that, she thought, someone who won't sleep until they've heard your voice. She gave herself a little shake. It's just the Valentine's Day atmosphere, she told herself, a touch of sentiment hanging in the air, but it will go away soon enough!

It looked bitterly cold outside, a heavy frost already glistening on the pavements. Snow had been forecast, and it looked like the weather men might be right, for once.

She shivered, and slid one arm into the sleeve of her coat, hoping Joe wouldn't be too much longer so they could get off home before the snow came down.

"Here, let me help you with that."

SUDDENLY Greg was beside her, holding out the other sleeve, helping her into her coat.

"I thought you'd gone ages ago," she said, her voice little more than a whisper.

"Not without saying goodnight." And, with that, he bent to pick up one of the balloons from the floor and presented it to her.

"Sorry I didn't bring roses, but I didn't know you'd be here. A little gift because it is Valentine's Day, after all."

"Only just. It'll all be over in a few minutes. Thank heavens!" Fran looked up at him uncertainly.

"I'd better do it now, then," Greg said, looking at his watch. "Before I miss my chance."

He leaned forward then, and kissed her very gently on the cheek. Fran stood frozen, unsure what to say.

"I thought maybe we could meet again," he said, his voice tumbling out in a rush. "What about tomorrow? When it's not Valentine's Day any more. We could meet as two people who – I hope – still care about each other, meeting up to say hello after a long time apart."

She gazed into his face, hugged the balloon to her chest, felt the hot flush rise in her cheek where his lips had been. She still couldn't think of anything to say, but her heart was doing that funny little quickstep again, just like it had earlier.

Greg hadn't finished.

"I've missed you, Fran. I don't know about you, but – well, Going Solo may be a great business idea, but it's not a way of life, is it?" He looked into her eyes. "Being single isn't all it's cracked up to be."

Out of the corner of her eye, she could just see Joe, shrinking back against the wall, trying to be discreet, but with a big "I told you so" grin all over his face.

She smiled then.

And, as Greg pulled her slowly towards him, the big red balloon she had been clutching so tightly burst with a very loud bang, and all three of them laughed and stepped out into the cold night air – just as the clock in the lobby behind them struck twelve. ■

Babe

A**DAPTED** from Dick King-Smith's novel "The Sheep-Pig", the 1995 film "Babe" is the tale of an orphan pig who is adopted by a sheepdog and then found to have a unique talent for herding sheep himself.

It was filmed entirely in Australia, and approximately forty-eight real Yorkshire pigs were used for the film along with an advanced animatronic pig created by Jim Henson's inimitable Creature Shop.

A make-up artist was hired to take care of the pigs for their appearances, adding toupée and eyelashes to each before their turn on camera! The film required so many pigs as during the six months of shooting, the young pigs would grow up too quickly to play the title rôle.

Nearly one thousand animals were involved in the film, which required over fifty animal trainers to co-ordinate.

By way of the tribute to the author, the sheepdog championship at the end of the film takes place at the Kingsmith Fairground and the electrician met on the way there is called Dick.

Praised for its originality as well as its appealing idea that good manners can get you a long way, especially with a little help from family and friends, "Babe" was a phenomenal critical success and was nominated for seven Oscars – including Best Picture – losing out only to "Braveheart" on the night.

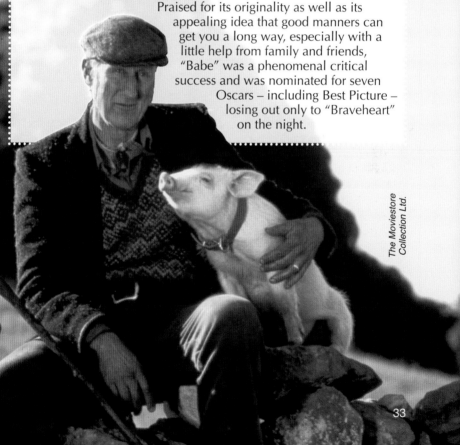

The Moviestore Collection Ltd.

The Helm Wind

by Alison Carter.

IN exotic parts of the world, people give names to their winds. The Sirocco, the Chinook, the Mistral. When people are at the mercy of nature they will give her a label, perhaps in the hope that she will be merciful.

In the British Isles there is only one named wind – the Helm Wind. The people who live along the beautiful slopes of Cross Fell in Cumbria know the Helm Wind well. It comes whenever it chooses, often in the spring when the world looks at its sweetest.

Their only warning is a solid bar of cloud which forms high above the fell. Then folk know that their lives will be taken over by the steady and ferocious wind that hurls itself across the villages of their part of the Eden Valley for hours, sometimes for days. It was always like this, before weather forecasts, when that country was Cumberland . . .

"It's a bright day, Mrs Wills." Robin Stanton had just stepped out of Fellerby post office and had come across his mother's friend. "I love April. There are a dozen different greens on the fells. It makes it feel worthwhile, living so far from civilisation."

Mrs Wills gathered her parcels to her expansive chest.

"I don't know about that. Fellerby is civilisation enough for me." She followed Robin's gaze up the slope, though, to the sunshine glancing along the peak. "And you can't be sure, even on a day like this, that the Helm Wind won't come and knock over those sheep, them silly things that don't know a thing about it, and take the blossoms of all that's blooming."

Robin smiled.

"That's true, Mrs Wills. Can I help you with your shopping?"

Mrs Wills's manner softened.

"Aye, that'd be good of you, Robin." She handed over a large collection of purchases, adjusted her hat and walked beside him.

ROBIN STANTON had lived in Fellerby all his life. He had trained to be a teacher at the college in Penrith, to his proud mother's delight. It was natural that he should take over the Fellerby school from Mr Carter, who was retiring and going to live with his sister who ran a boarding-house at Grange-over-Sands.

Robin loved his village, the largest along the fell, and he loved the children in his care. He played football with the scant team of young men that could be mustered from the farms and villages, and had what he felt was a good life in a comfortable house with his mother, a widow. But as the new century

35

ripened, Robin wondered about a house of his own, and a young woman to live in it with him.

I T was quite a day when the Jones family came to Fellerby.

"I was told that a gentleman from Manchester was coming to close up the feather-works," his mother told Robin one evening. "But it appears that this Mr Jones has brought his whole family with him!"

"With children who'll want a temporary place at the school?" Robin asked.

"No. There is just one daughter, of at least twenty, Mrs Wills reports. A young woman of the latest fashion." Mrs Stanton gave this last news with a faint tone of disapproval.

Fashion was not something much respected among the matrons of Fellerby. It was best kept, they felt, to the streets of Manchester.

"How long will these Joneses stay?" Robin asked her.

"I suppose it will be several weeks. It's a big place to sort out. The works cover several acres. But at least those who were still working will be found other jobs by this Manchester man, or will be retiring."

"I will be glad to meet the family."

His mother glanced sideways at him.

"I don't imagine you will like the young woman," she said quickly. "Mrs Wills spoke of a lack of . . ." Mrs Stanton coughed. "That is, she spoke of a bold striped jacket and a lack of corsetry."

Robin smiled to himself. Miss Jones was not likely to be a success among the older ladies of Fellerby.

The green at Fellerby had once been noisy with the great flocks of geese which supplied the local pillow and mattress industry. Some residents could remember the geese before they were moved to be farmed in a more modern way at the new works. Some could recall their grandparents talking of wrestling on the green, way back.

Now, the village was quieter, and last year it had been decided that the feather-works must close. The industry was growing near the ports where goods could be easily imported. The villages of the fells would revert to farming. Mr Jones had come from the city firm that had acquired the site, to close the works and make such profit as he could from the equipment and the land. Robin learned that he had brought his wife and daughter for a "holiday" at Fellerby because it was spring and good walking weather.

Robin met Miss Jones by chance. It was a Friday afternoon, and warm. He had sent the children off home and taken himself for a long walk up towards the Hartside Pass. But he was hardly tired when he returned, eight miles later, to the edge of the village.

"Is it flat, do you think?" A cheerful female voice made him stop abruptly and spin round to look towards the small field behind the churchyard.

"Flat?" he asked, guessing the person peering over the high wall must be the famous Miss Jones.

"I mean this bit of land, of course. Come over and give me your opinion."

This was the sort of young woman who didn't ask, but commanded. Robin climbed over the stile and stood looking blankly at primroses and cowpats.

"If we're to be here for a season, I mean to make a tennis court. There must be people who play tennis. I'm Lucinda Jones. Who are you?"

Robin took the small hand boldly offered, and shook it.

"Robin Stanton, teacher."

She laughed.

"You sound like you're giving evidence in a court of law! Well, Robin Stanton, teacher, can you lob, can you volley?"

Lucinda Jones was a slight young woman with thick dark hair worn pinned in a loose and (to Robin) bewitching style. She had dark blue eyes and a figure that he didn't imagine could be improved by the corsets his mother considered so important.

Later that day, when Robin had escorted her back to the Joneses's large rented house at the top of the village, he thought to himself that she was a breath of fresh air. Then he corrected himself. Fellerby had plenty of fresh air. She was a breath of exotic perfume!

MISS JONES turned out to light up everything she passed by, in Robin's opinion, to lift every head like a breeze on a hot day. She made Mrs Stanton look askance at her new ideas and her exuberance, and caused Robin to seek her company. There was no great variety of social events in Fellerby and district, so they were thrown together at most gatherings.

Miss Jones altered everything she touched.

"Well!" she exclaimed to Robin when he handed her the invitation for the Easter social in the church hall. "I don't know why there's no dancing!"

"I suppose they have no musicians," Robin said.

She looked up at him, impatience glinting in her blue eyes.

"You play the piano!"

"I teach, using the hall piano," he corrected, "but –"

"But nothing. You can play. I've also met the grumpy but presumably talented Miss Brough from Melmerby, who claims to play the fiddle and confesses to the occasional waltz. And my mother has a cello, which she will dust off if I am very nice to her. So, a trio!"

✻   ✻   ✻   ✻

The tennis court area was mown by the verger, who found himself unable to refuse Miss Jones. Afterwards, he stood mute as she and Robin Stanton handed him bundles of canvas strips.

"To mark the court," she said brightly.

Tennis was played, and when that palled Miss Jones organised a football tournament. She recruited men from six to seventy-six.

The weather stayed fine, and whatever the elders of the district thought privately, there was much fun to be had in Fellerby that spring.

"She's like the wind," Robin said to himself one morning, unaware his mother was in the room. "You can't tell where she'll blow next."

"I beg your pardon, Robin?" his mother asked, her hand hovering above the teapot.

"Nothing, Mother."

Miss Jones's parents were welcoming towards Robin. They were kind, cheerful people who invited him for suppers, and seemed to encourage the two

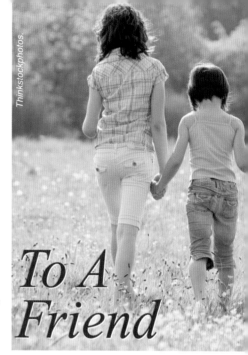

To A Friend

young people to be together. After less than a month Robin was deeply in love with the exotic hint of perfume, the unexpected breeze that was Lucinda Jones.

He adored the way she forced the more conservative residents of Fellerby to like her; the way she added the perfect flower to another girl's hat; the picnic she organised with the schoolchildren for which they had to dress up as a historical character; the way she begged the Parish Council so incessantly to do something about the plainness of the green that they eventually gave in and planted a line of birches.

He loved her.

IT was the Helm Wind that made Robin finally speak. The thick tell-tale bar of cloud rolled in one May evening.

"My goodness, what's that?" Lucinda and Robin were standing beside the birch saplings. He had suggested a walk, and Lucinda, always keen to be "up and doing", had agreed.

"The Helm Wind is coming," he said. "Probably tonight."

"You sound like some harbinger of doom!" She laughed and placed a hand on Robin's arm, and for a moment he was in heaven. "How bad can a wind be?"

Robin smiled. He took her home, and was invited, as so often before, to stay for tea. He tried to explain about the Helm Wind, but the family was talking about the feather-works, and plying Robin with cake.

And then, from nowhere, came the howl of the wind as it hit the side of the solid house. They all rushed to the window as the blooms were blown from the bed of pink azaleas as though brushed away by a giant hand, and as the

WALK with me through the
springtime,
Through the budding of the year,
And walk with me in the summer
When skies are blue and clear.
And through the autumn glory,
The orange, red and brown,
Be with me, sharing cheerful
   thoughts,
Though leaves are tumbling down.

Walk with me in the winter
Through the fog or frost and snow,
We'll catch the sunshine when we can
And watch the snowdrops grow.
Through all the passing seasons,
Through changing time and tide,
We'll share the precious joys of life,
For ever side by side.

– Iris Hesselden.

fence separating the garden from the lane strained in its fixings. The village seemed to be hanging on for dear life as it was pushed inexorably in one direction.

"Good heavens, it sounds like an express train to London!" Mr Jones said.

"Like a pack of angry old wolves," Lucinda added, standing close to Robin. It seemed even she, always bold and cheerful, was made nervous by the strangeness of this. He longed to put an arm around her.

"Let's see what's happening on the other side of the house," she suggested.

Five minutes later they stood together on an upper landing. Her face was close to the tall sash window, and her softly falling white dress and motionless figure formed a sharp contrast with the darkness outside, the shriek of the wind, the destruction. Tiny sheep on the fell battled to stay standing as the steady force of the Helm Wind battered them.

It was a strange evening, though Robin knew the wind of old. He turned to look at her. A full minute passed before she realised he wasn't looking through the window. She turned to face him.

"You must know," Robin said quickly. "You must have noticed . . ." He stopped, seeing her simple, enquiring expression. A feeling of dread seized him but he couldn't stop now. "You must have realised that I love you."

She stepped away from the window, away from him. The wind pushed at the glass beside her as she stared.

"Oh, dear. I've given you the wrong . . . Robin, I'm engaged!"

He held the banister for support as if the Helm Wind had found him, too. "Engaged!"

"To my Justin, back home in Manchester. Justin is a lawyer, a graduate of Cambridge. At least, he will be a lawyer – maybe even the bar – when he finishes his studies. Justin is very clever and . . . oh, this is not helping, of course." She looked at the stair carpet. "Robin, if I gave you any . . . if I passed too much time with you . . ." Her head hung low.

Robin took a deep breath.

"Please say no more about it. I must be going."

"Not in this!" Her voice was a whisper, scarcely audible above the roar of the wind.

"It can't knock me down," he said dully. "Look at the sheep. I can stay standing."

He made an excuse to Mr and Mrs Jones and left. Despite his words, he didn't know how he could stay standing.

MRS JONES called on Robin Stanton a few days later. She walked through a village desolated by the wind, stripped to its skeleton, but didn't mention it when she was shown into the parlour by Robin. He silently offered her a chair, but she shook her head.

"Lucinda," she said with an effort, turning a broad, feathered hat in her hands, "is very distressed. No more than we are – Mr Jones and myself. I think we are friends enough that I can be candid and say that we were as much to blame as our daughter in . . . in possibly encouraging you."

She swallowed.

"Lucinda is bright, and well, a force of nature, shall we say. But she is young. She thinks she loves this Justin Mayfield, and also thinks that she has promised him everything. He is, however, a lazy, conceited man who is spending his father's income and has no interest in his career. My husband suspects that he is . . . involved with another girl. We did nothing to keep you apart. We are sorry. The intention was that only my husband come here on this business with the feather-works, but I judged it a good idea to bring Lucinda on a little holiday to see if we could perhaps make her forget Mayfield."

Robin was silent. He felt he ought to be angry at what they had done, or had failed to do. But he hadn't the energy.

"Lucinda sees the best in everyone," Mrs Jones went on, as if in explanation.

"Not in me," he said quietly.

"Oh, she does!" Mrs Jones stood suddenly and approached Robin. "It was why we didn't keep you apart. She liked you immediately . . ."

They both jumped at the sound of the front door. Mrs Stanton entered, bustling with news from around the village.

"I suppose you've come to talk about the wind's work, Mrs Jones."

The other woman smiled weakly.

"Of a sort," she replied. "One that blows through and does damage, while hardly meaning to."

Mrs Stanton stood astonished as Mrs Jones politely left.

THE feather-works was closed down more quickly than anticipated. Mr Jones was good at his work. As spring passed into summer, great carts and a large motor van moved the equipment down the valley. Soon afterwards came a car to take the Jones family and their trunks.

Mrs Jones had worked hard to make life less awkward for both her daughter and Robin Stanton. She kept social contact light and infrequent. Villagers wondered if Miss Jones was unwell, since the wave of activity that went everywhere with her lessened so dramatically.

The family drove away as a summer shower began to fall, and Robin Stanton watched them from the schoolroom window as the children worked at their arithmetic.

The rain continued into a wet and miserable summer. Robin tried to distract himself with work. The line of birches mocked him. The tennis court, muddy and dishevelled, matched his mood. Summer turned, almost without anyone noticing, into a damp and misty autumn.

Robin taught piano, but closed the lid as soon as the last pupil left the hall. He walked the fells and tried not to think of Lucinda Jones.

It was a freezing November morning when a hired horse cab drew up on the track beside the green. The horse steamed as it stood, restless, on the ice. From the interior emerged two fashionable women, tightly wrapped in furs. The elder stood talking to the younger for a minute, holding both her hands, and then kissed her and turned aside to enter the church porch.

The younger woman watched her go and then walked slowly, almost reluctantly, towards the Stanton cottage.

*　*　*　*

"I would have brought Mother in if I'd dared," Lucinda Jones said quietly to Robin. His mother, mystified, had just closed the door behind her, leaving them alone. "But she says that, if I'm the modern woman I say I am, who makes her own decisions, and her own mistakes, then it's my task alone."

She looked nervous, small and very beautiful to Robin, hanging on her every word. He felt he might begin to shake as he stood there, pens and papers scattered on the floor about his feet. On hearing her voice in the hall he'd stood up so suddenly he had sent them flying.

"I've been a fool," she whispered, "and a bad judge of character. Until today. That man whom I thought I . . . well, he was just not worth –"

But before she could finish Robin was across the twelve feet that separated them and had taken her in his arms.

"I loved you from the moment I saw you."

"And I think I loved you, in the field among the cowslips."

"Primroses."

She laughed, though it was almost a sob.

"But I had to finish with being a girl and start being a woman."

"Never be anything but what you are," he told her. "My own wild wind."

She drew back, staring at him.

"Like the Helm Wind? Wrecking everything?"

He laughed.

"Yes, the Helm Wind; that is, a wonderful force of nature that I can't predict."

She kissed him.

"And that will always return to here, and only here. To where you are." ▮

Illustration by Richard Eraut.

Seeking A Fair Maiden

by Marilyn Fountain.

April 1963

I **ESPY** the dragon!" she screamed, and the gauzy sleeve of her white dress billowed as she pointed down to the town.

"Gadzooks, 'tis true! And methought the beast securely despatched by my trusty blade." And he waved his foil-covered cardboard sword above his head.

George and the Fair Maiden shared an amused glance, until George's visor – which he'd been having trouble with all day – snapped shut, and the pair of them fell about laughing. Two of the major players in the town's annual St George's Day event, they were atop Strawberry Hill, where they'd escaped to after the dramatic rescue.

42

With his helmet and her pointed hat removed, they sat on the grass and hugged their knees, just a couple of modern teenagers again, fifteen going on sixteen. Below them, the sinking sun was gilding the rooftops of Leavenbury, and the happy crowds were drifting home.

Barbara suddenly shivered. Mike wondered if he dared put his arm around her.

"This is probably the last time I'll see this view," she murmured. "To think that this time tomorrow, I'll be heading for the other side of the world."

Mike didn't want to think about it, but it had dominated his thoughts ever since he'd learned Barbara's restless father had decided to relocate the family to Australia. Mike ached to be a few years older.

"What are you going to miss most?" he asked, annoyed with himself for not having the nerve to ask "who" instead.

"Everything, I suppose. I mean, I'm excited about going, who wouldn't be, but –" She turned to look at him and her misty-blue eyes caused the breath to catch in his throat.

"But – ?" he prompted croakily.

"The people," she replied shyly. "I'm going to miss the people most of all. I don't expect they have St George's day in Australia, do they?"

"Probably not," he whispered back, still unable to tear his eyes away from her face.

April 2013

D ID you ever see a dream walking? Well, I did." That was a funny old song his grandad sometimes sang and now Andy knew what it really meant. The dream that was sauntering along Leavenbury's Market Street was the most beautiful girl he'd ever seen.

Tall and slim, her long golden hair streamed out like a banner in the breeze. He just had to ask her. She could only say no, couldn't she?

"Excuse me, fair maiden."

Carly jumped when the dark-haired lad brushed her arm to attract her attention. She'd seen him earlier, gazing at her across the Market Square, but she'd pretended not to notice and carried on admiring the quaint town buildings, so different from the modern Federation Square in Melbourne. But then all thoughts of home fell away, and all she was aware of was a pair of expressive green-brown eyes searching her face.

"If you're not doing anything this afternoon, I wonder how you'd feel about being rescued from a dragon's fire-breathing jaws by a chivalrous mediaeval knight on a silver charger?"

She burst out laughing.

"Well, whad'ya know! I wasn't expecting that."

He blinked.

"And I wasn't expecting that accent. You're from Australia?"

"Sure am. Does being from Oz mean I don't qualify for rescuing?"

"Certainly not! In fact, it can only enrich your experience of English culture and tradition. You mean you'd be willing to do it?"

"Depends. What would I have to do?"

"How's your swooning?" He grinned.

She smiled back. If only he knew she was doing a fair bit of that inside already.

N**ANA!** You'll never guess what I'm going to be doing this arvo . . . "
When Carly breezed back into the teashop, Barbara was sitting in the sunny window alcove and gazing dreamily out over the Market Place, thinking how half a century ago felt just like yesterday, now that she was back.

Although not Leavenbury born and bred, from the day she'd left, this was the place she'd kept in her heart as home. The man she'd married was an Australian through and through but he had often expressed a wish to see the country of her birth.

She sighed, feeling a renewed pang of loss, even though she'd been widowed five years now. Her granddaughter, Carly, had initiated the idea, because the girl planned to study in England next year and wanted to visit some of the colleges in advance.

And they couldn't come all this way without a detour to Leavenbury, particularly as it happened to be April again. Much had changed, of course, but from the advertising poster Barbara had glimpsed by the cake counter, the town's St George's Day celebrations were still going strong – and she recalled Mike, who had been so handsome as her chivalrous St George. She'd often wondered how his life had turned out. What might he be doing now?

* * * *

"Andy, your sister's going to be all right." Mike had gone outside the hospital building to call his grandson. "It's only a very slight fracture, so they'll be putting her arm in plaster later this morning and then we can leave. With any luck, we should be back to see your St George – that's if there's going to be one now?"

"Yes, there is. But no thanks to Anna. What a day to fall off her bike!"

"I don't think she did it deliberately." Mike sighed.

Peace-making had been his wife Lilian's rôle when they'd moved back to Leavenbury to be closer to the family, but when they'd lost her, he'd taken it on. Andy and Anna had been youngsters then, and he was still doing it. At this rate, his grandchildren would still be squabbling when they were in their forties, and he was in his dotage!

"No, Pops, I know," Andy replied, making Mike curious as to why he was sounding so cheerful. "I hope she's not in too much pain, and tell her not to worry too much about letting everyone down!"

"Oh, Andy!"

"Only joking, Pops. I've found the perfect understudy. This absolutely stunning girl was in the Market Place this morning. I thought I was seeing things for a minute, as if she'd been conjured up from my imagination or something. But she's real enough, and her name is Carly, and she's agreed to be the Fair Maiden for this afternoon's pageant."

"Well done, lad!" Mike was taken aback. Andy had never spoken so enthusiastically as this about any other girl before. "You're sure the young lady knows what she's letting herself in for?"

"I've told her what to expect and she's still all for it. Not like the local girls who all turned me down. Perhaps it's because she's an Aussie that Carly's got more of a sense of adventure."

"An Aussie?"

Whenever Australia cropped up in conversation or on the news, an image of a beautiful flaxen-haired, blue-eyed girl called Barbara Evans fluttered through his mind.

AND this is my nana." Carly introduced Barbara to Andy's mum, Wendy.

The back room where the performers in the pageant were getting ready was noisy pandemonium. Andy, rigged out in chain mail, topped by a white tabard painted with the cross of St George, was already clanking his way to the Abbey stables to collect his steed. He would be riding into town directly from there.

"Pleased to meet you," a harassed-looking Wendy declared, while trying to team up green-trousered Boy Scouts by height to avoid a lopsided dragon. "It's so good of your granddaughter to step in as Fair Maiden at the last minute."

Barbara glanced at Carly. Now dressed in the maiden's costume of long white dress, chain girdle and tall white hat with floating veil, she was clearly relishing the experience.

"Wild dragons wouldn't have stopped her from taking part! Especially when she realised how gorgeous that outfit is. And I think your son proved quite an attraction, too!" she added.

"Andy can be very persuasive sometimes." Wendy's expression was rueful, but proud. "At Christmas he talked me into 'just lending a hand' on the St George's Day committee, and I've not had a moment's peace since! Still, it'll be worth it, as long as everything goes to plan."

"Well, let me lend you a hand now, then."

Barbara stepped forward to help her spread out the dragon's skin on the floor.

"I'm so pleased to see Leavenbury's still upholding the St George's Day traditions."

"Oh, yes, Carly mentioned you used to live here once. You ought to talk to my dad. He was born here, although he eventually moved away for work. Are you catching up with relatives in the area?"

"I've got a couple of distant cousins on the south coast who're expecting us tomorrow. But mainly we're over here to check out colleges for Carly and took a short diversion. She wants to study fashion here next year."

"Andy's taking a year out to earn some money, and then he's off to university this autumn," Wendy said. She bent down to grip one half of the costume, and Barbara took hold of the other.

"Ready?" Wendy prompted, and when Barbara nodded, they lifted the skin over the line of waiting Scouts. "Stand still now, boys . . ."

IT was time for Carly to climb the steps to the maiden's bower at the top of the Market Cross building. Barbara adjusted the girdle so that it draped flatteringly around her hips.

"Ta, Nana. Anyone would think you've done this before!"

"Actually, I have," Barbara admitted, the memories flooding back thick and fast now. Carly wasn't showing a fraction of the nerves that she'd felt on the day.

"You never said."

"I played the Fair Maiden here fifty years ago, I wasn't going to say anything because I didn't want to steal your thunder."

"What a corker! Just wait till I tell Andy, he'll be as made up as me. He's well into tradition and all that . . . in fact, he said – "

Barbara smiled. Her granddaughter had learned quite a lot about this young man in a very short space of time. But she and Carly were leaving Leavenbury in the morning and the girl couldn't lose her heart in a day, could she? Silly question, really!

"Carly, I thought you'd already gone!" Wendy's voice was full of panic. "St George is already at the top of the High Street and I've just sent out the dragon. They'll have no-one to fight over!"

"'Struth!" Clutching the hem of her skirt in one hand, and holding her hat on with the other, the modern Fair Maiden dashed athletically off to the Market Cross.

The bunting-bedecked Market Square was packed with spectators, currently being entertained by a troupe of Morris dancers and musicians in period costumes playing mediaeval instruments. Barbara squeezed her way

Gorillas In The Mist

THE true story of conservationist Dian Fossey was the subject of the 1988 hit film "Gorillas In The Mist". Loosely based on her life, the film covers Dian's fateful meeting with Dr Louis Leakey and her establishment of a research centre in Rwanda to observe the native gorillas. Fossey was charged with performing an in-depth study of the gorillas' habits and their society.

To get close enough to do this, though, required thousands of hours of time spent with them to gain their trust and acceptance. This momentous occasion came when, in 1970, after nearly two and a half years spent amongst them, an adult male called Peanuts reached out to touch her hand.

Although the film itself is full of real gorilla footage, for some of the close-contact scenes gorilla suits were employed with folk inside them!

Dian's legacy to the mountain gorillas continues in the work of the Dian Fossey Gorilla Fund International, who work hard to protect a species threatened by poaching, armed conflict and the encroaching of humans on their natural habitat.

The Moviestore Collection Ltd.

47

through to catch a glimpse of proceedings.

The approaching sounds of a big bass drum accompanying a marching brass band signalled the imminent highlight of the day's celebrations. The dancers took a bow and stepped aside with a jangle of bells, allowing a herald in a red and yellow tabard to take centre stage. He lifted a horn to his lips and blew a triumphant phrase.

Barbara shielded her eyes from the sun to look up at the top of the Market Cross. Carly looked an absolute picture, serenely waving a handkerchief. Barbara waved excitedly back, not sure whether she could be seen or not as the crowds swayed continually around her.

ACROSS the other side of the square, Anna exclaimed to her grandad, "Look at the Fair Maiden. Isn't she doing a brilliant job? I'd have just wanted to laugh."

Mike thought the girl playing the Fair Maiden was all but perfect in the rôle. In his mind, there would only ever be one Fair Maiden, and that was Barbara. But this year's representative was the closest yet, in fact, uncannily similar. . .

"An Aussie", Andy had said she was. The words seemed to drum in his ears along with the beat from the musical instruments. Gazing in the direction of the crowds opposite, a waving hand caught his attention. From a blur of faces, one seemed to loom into focus for a fraction of a second . . .

Small, pale-haired, there was something about the way the woman had lifted her head that struck a chord. He felt an aching in his chest as he desperately tried to pick her out again from the swirling crowd.

The dragon was prowling forward now and the crowd, getting into the mood, booed and hissed. The beast swung round, biting and lunging. Suddenly it lifted its great head and roared, exhaling a plume of grey smoke. The Fair Maiden clutched the rails of the bower and let out an ear-splitting scream.

Mike steadied Anna as she wobbled when someone brushed past her. She'd insisted he bring her to the pageant, even though the hospital had said she should really go straight home and rest her arm. He could see from her expression that the painkillers were starting to wear off.

"Come on, young lady, I think you've had enough for now."

"Oh, just a few more minutes, please. Here comes Andy, and I must see if he can stay on that horse."

Into the square rode the dashing St George, one hand on the reins of a sturdy white horse, the other waving a sword above his head. The audience cheered. St George and the Dragon circled round each other, countering lunges and swipes with ducks and swerves. At last the decisive blow hit home and the dragon was symbolically slain, and the triumphant knight disappeared inside the Market Cross.

Barbara glanced over at the spectators opposite. It was hard to be sure in a shifting crowd, but she thought she caught a glimpse of a girl with an arm in plaster standing just in front of a tall man. Could that possibly be Andy's unfortunate sister? Perhaps she'd got back in time to watch it, after all? Barbara searched again, but she couldn't pinpoint the spot any more.

S T GEORGE had emerged from the Market Cross now, his arm gently round the Fair Maiden. He lifted her gently on to the waiting horse, and off they went, to the approving applause of the satisfied spectators. Barbara wiped a tear from her eyes; despite the whole occasion being so much more elaborate and ambitious than the simple scene she and Mike had performed, it had still brought back all the emotion of that long-ago day.

"I'm sorry your sis wasn't able to do it," Carly told Andy.

They'd changed back into their everyday clothes and were helping Barbara and Wendy pack away the costumes for next year.

"I'm not!" he replied. "Do you think anyone noticed that my helmet visor kept slipping down?"

"Only me!" Carly laughed.

"Andy, I've not told you yet. Nana was in the St George's Day pageant here . . . oh, how many years ago, Nana?"

"Too many," Barbara replied softly.

"So was my grandad!" Andy exclaimed. "I don't know when exactly, but we can ask him. Is Pops still planning to come down this evening?"

Barbara found she was holding her breath for his mother's response.

"I think he's intending to keep Anna company until we get back. They were in the town earlier, though, and saw your star performances. They were very impressed with the pair of you."

"That's a shame," Andy told Carly, including Barbara in the conversation. "I'd have liked you to have met Pops. Perhaps tomorrow?"

"We're leaving first thing," Barbara said, her own sinking heart echoing the look of dismay on Carly's face.

Of course her granddaughter was lamenting having to leave Andy so soon. But Barbara suspected their blossoming friendship wouldn't be severed. She thought Andy was a smashing young man and Carly would be back in England next year. Meanwhile, there was always e-mail. The world was a much smaller place now than it had been when she was a teenager.

"Andy?" Barbara asked. "I just wondered if I might have known him. What is his name?"

"Pops's name? It's –"

The door to the room opened and everyone looked up to see who it was.

"Mike!" Barbara breathed. He'd changed, of course, but it was still him.

"Barbara! I thought it was you in the crowd this afternoon, but I kept telling myself it couldn't be."

Then they were running across the floor to an embrace that had waited fifty years. ∎

The Good Life

by Frosty Ivermee.

WHAT on earth was I thinking? A grown man trying to duck out of sight behind the gooseberry bushes. It was doubly foolish as I not only ended up with scratched knees, but I also looked ridiculous.

I scowled over the bushes at the path leading to plot number eleven, where a spritely looking pair of legs, encased in red wellies, were coming across the grass.

The city allotments were surrounded by houses with many gardens backing on to them, and this new plot owner had managed to secure the site next to mine. She unlocked her shed with a casual air, turned round and saw me, frowned deeply and looked away.

Well, that suited me fine. I just didn't want any company today.

All the plots were lined up closely with narrow paths in between, which were either made of grass in various lengths and neatness, or had bark chips shovelled over to discourage weeds.

I used to come here to dig and plant in peace and that was one of the reasons I had come so often lately – I needed to be by myself. But with demand for organic on the increase, and the rising price of fruit and veg, it seemed that everyone and his dog wanted a taste of the good life.

Most plots had a shed of some sort, and Red Wellies had inherited one, sturdy enough, from the previous owner. She had evidently already moved in a variety of garden implements. I could see a garden fork, a hoe and a large tub of plant food now through the small window. She clumped purposefully past, swinging her watering can, grass swishing against her legs.

She ignored me completely.

There was already a little patch of bare earth at the far end, near the water trough, where she'd begun to cultivate her plot. I tried not to feel invaded. I still badly wanted to finish planting out my beans. The ground was prepared to a fine tilth stretching right across the width of the plot and all the bamboo canes were in place.

I felt the usual satisfaction looking at the straight rows. They were something I could look after and it was always like magic to see the tiny seeds spring to life. I risked a glance at plot eleven and saw the blonde head, peppered with grey, busy watering, and suddenly I couldn't decide whether to get on with the planting or head for home.

My sister, June, would not have approved if she could have seen me scuttling about hiding and avoiding people.

"You want to get out more, Paul," she had implored on her last visit. "And I

Illustration by Mandy Dixon.

51

don't mean that old allotment," she'd said firmly, as I'd opened my mouth to defend myself. "I mean restaurants, cinemas – hairdressers." She'd raised her eyebrows pointedly in the direction of my head, which I had to admit needed a going over with the lawn-mower.

June had suddenly grabbed my hand.

"Look, love, I know it's hard, but you have to start to move on or you'll end up with only potatoes for company!"

After she'd gone, I'd thought about what she'd said, and reluctantly admitted that she had a point. I had been spending more time alone lately. I'd never been good at dealing with my feelings, and I always seemed to make everything worse by holding things in or avoiding them altogether.

I suppose I got that from my dad. He was a bit like that at times. These days, people didn't seem to chat face to face, but through social networking sites, like MyFace and YooHoo, or whatever they were called. I had joined the band of silver surfers but I didn't go on the computer much. In the end, the pull of the outdoors always won.

Even as a child, I had revelled in the feeling of the fresh air around me, my heart seeming to expand as I looked at the ever-changing scenes spread out before me like a carpet beneath the colours of the sky.

But June was right – I was in a rut, and my troubles at the allotment were just the tip of the iceberg. It took me somewhat by surprise to realise it, and I dug my fork crossly into the soil, turning up a few surprised worms as I did so.

I was so lost in thought that I didn't notice the flash of red until it was disappearing down the path towards the gates.

Good riddance, I thought. Now I can get on.

But somehow the day had lost its appeal and, annoyed with myself, I stomped off home.

THE next day, I went to the allotment early, keen to make up for lost time.

"Look behind you!" Red Wellies chuckled.

I turned in time to see a robin fly from the handle of my spade where it had been perched expectantly.

"Looks like you've found a friend." She was looking at me kindly.

There was a pause.

"I'm sorry – for everything," I said.

She looked at me steadily, her blue eyes giving nothing away.

"I know I was being unreasonable," I continued. "It's just that the allotment has always been *my* thing. My escape from everything – not you," I hastened to add, as I saw her face drop. "But when you got a plot, too, next to mine, it changed things, and you know I've always been terrible at handling change." I thought back to the most recent change of all, the death of my beloved father.

Pot Of Primulas

I'VE bought a pot of primulas to place upon my sill,
A splash of joyful colour, just to warm the winter's chill.
So when the skies are leaden and it's raining a monsoon,
I'll gaze upon the primulas and know that very soon
Bright spring will step upon the stage, will smile, and take a bow,
But meanwhile pretty primulas will cheer me here and now.

— *Maggie Ingall.*

I knew that she understood. She always knew me so well.

But lately I had been stubborn, refusing to make amends after our silly argument just because she'd decided to get a plot of her own. She'd been wanting to join me on my plot for months now, so she could have a small space to grow things – we were too overlooked by neighbouring trees at home to grow veg there. But I had childishly clung to my belief that the allotment was my escape and so, without really meaning to, had always put her off.

In a sudden rush, I was ashamed to realise that I had been shutting her out, not only since our row blew up three days ago, but also since Dad had died several months before. It had shocked me to realise how much I'd missed him. It was bad enough when Mum had passed away the previous year, but with both parents gone, I felt bereft.

I fought back a tightening in my throat as I struggled to explain.

"When you were here with me yesterday, I began to realise that things had changed, but for the better. I loved you being here, Daisy."

My wife smiled and, in a few seconds, she was in my arms. I breathed in the scent of her hair, and trembled with relief.

I pulled back to look at her.

"And June was right, we do need to start going out more. I don't want to waste another minute of this life with you." I paused, pulled off my old hat and smiled impishly, my hair standing out at all angles. "And to start with that means a good haircut!"

For the rest of the day, we tended the ground together, and talked as we had not done in a long time. Later, we brought out the camping stove and, while the kettle boiled for a cup of tea, I had my first haircut in months! As the first grey and white tufts floated gently to the ground in the late, golden afternoon sunlight, we watched as the red robin took some strands in his beak for a nest.

OVER the summer, we began to go out more and I felt myself unfurl, as if I had only been half awake before. Restaurants were enjoyed, old friends sought out and we even threw a party for my birthday.

At the allotments, we had a glut of strawberries and stuffed ourselves with the sweet, scarlet globes, giggling like a couple of kids as juice ran down our chins.

Meanwhile, the plots continued to grow. I watched in delight as tendrils of courgettes and pumpkin plants scrambled across the path from number eleven, spilling into and rumpling the order and neatness of mine.

Great swathes of sweet-peas sprang up like fireworks. Daisy had even planted some around my upright beans, and they were now exploding with colour and scent. Day after day, we stood together and marvelled as giant sunflowers stretched up and created vast silhouettes, which seemed to us to own the sky.

There were nasturtiums, too, which billowed, jostled for space, and flowered in great blobs of orange, tempting all kinds of insects. After a downpour, the disc-shaped leaves around the flowers held glistening raindrops, and we were spellbound for, despite our social lives being more full, we still made time to come here and enjoy the quiet beauty of the allotments.

One afternoon, after our now traditional, steaming cuppa from the camping kettle, we were discussing seed catalogues as we polished off the last of the raspberries.

"You know, you're like the cat that's got the cream." Daisy grinned at me, her blue eyes twinkling.

"Funny, that," I said, scraping the last of the remnants of my dessert out of the dish. "I was just thinking, I'm so glad you got yourself a plot next to mine."

Daisy turned to look at me, raising her eyebrows and smiling questioningly.

"Yes," I continued, "and seeing you looking through all those catalogues, I've realised why. This is just a taste of the good life to come!" ■

Spring In Her Step

by Vicki Rendall.

SARAH stared at the daffodils. They were a much bigger bunch than any of the ones she had seen in the supermarket. The leaves were deep emerald green and the petals glowed, the central trumpet a burst of orange. These flowers were one of her favourite things about Easter. The problem was, she had no idea why they were on her doorstep, or who had put them there.

She picked up the bouquet and took it indoors. Examining the Cellophane and ribbon, she decided that they couldn't have been outside for too long. The air was chilly that morning and, although the water in the bottom of the wrapping was cold, the flowers were not. Perhaps the postman had delivered it?

She rang her daughter.

"People don't post flowers, Mum," Lucy pointed out.

"I suppose not. But the doorbell didn't ring. I only discovered they were there when I saw them through the glass. I thought it was next door's Labrador. Was it you? Did you drop them off for me?'

"Not me. I haven't got time to do drive-by flower deliveries. I've got to be at work for eight."

Lucy taught English at the local comprehensive and, although classes didn't start until nine, she always liked to be in early to take in waifs and strays from the breakfast club and to get her desk into a manageable order.

"Isn't there a card at all?" Lucy asked.

"Can't see one – no, wait. There is!" Sarah turned the daffodils around. A small, oblong card nestled in the centre, attached to a thin piece of wire. On its front was a cartoon rabbit throwing a carrot over his shoulder, preferring instead a large pile of Easter eggs. *To Someone Special* was printed along the top of the card in bold pink. On the back was a sticky label from one of the nicer florists in the town. Sarah described it to Lucy.

"Ooh! Someone's got an admirer!"

Sarah laughed.

"Oh, I don't think so. It's probably a mistake, and anyway, your father –"

"Dad's been gone five years now, Mum. It's OK to have someone else like you. Look, I've got to go. Last day of term – I need to prepare for battle!"

Sarah thought about what her daughter had said. It was five years since Pete had died and he would have hated to think she wasn't making the most of her life. She was still fairly young, and she did get lonely in the evenings. But she still couldn't be certain that the gift was meant for her. Her friend, Bev, would be able to shed some light. She was always the first person Sarah went to if she needed advice or a gossip.

A T the sports centre, Bev and Sarah took their usual spots at the back of the fitness studio. Lying on their backs with one leg in the air, Bev gave her verdict.

"I think," she whispered, "that it's definitely from a man and I think it's from a man that knows you well."

"How did you work that one out?" Sarah hissed as they pulled their knees into their chests. Hers gave a loud crunch. Bev giggled.

"Because a florist would have rung your doorbell. The person knows where you actually live and they got you your favourite. Although that could just be a lucky guess, I suppose . . ." The women twisted their hips from side to side.

"Who, then? Someone from the golf club?"

Bev glanced at her speculatively.

"Alan's single."

"Alan has been single for as long as I've known him, which is a long time. I think it's because he still lives with his mum."

"But he's sixty!"

"Exactly."

Bev considered.

"I'd have put money on it being Jim. He's always looking at you in the bar. But it can't be. He's away on a cruise. With a woman. From the internet."

Sarah raised her eyebrows. Lucy had persuaded her to try online dating the previous year, but she had realised quickly that what had been on screen and what turned up in person were not always the same thing. Sarah had to admit she was warming to the idea of a secret admirer.

In the café after their class, the two women settled down to tea and a shared chocolate muffin. Sarah pulled the card from her pocket.

"Not much to go on, really," Bev observed. "He's obviously got a sense of humour and, judging by where he bought the flowers, a bit of taste. It's a nice florist, this one."

Sarah took a sip of tea whilst she watched the cogs turn in Bev's head.

"I've got it! What about Graham? He asked me the other day how you were doing. He used to run that car-hire business for weddings and things. I wondered why he had been up to the club more often. It's you!" Bev grinned widely, pleased with what she saw as case solved. Sarah was not convinced.

Graham was handsome, friendly and, if the stories in the bar were right, about as good at golf as she was, which was terrible. It made her like the idea of him: a gentleman who wasn't perfect but just himself. Like Pete had been.

Bev spoke candidly through a mouthful of cake.

"Widowed five years, just like you, except it looks like he's not living in the past as much."

Bev dropped Sarah back at her house. The journey had been punctuated with reasons from Bev about why Graham would be a good catch.

As she was getting out of the car, Bev called after her, "Remember tonight. Seven-thirty pick-up. No excuses." She drove off before Sarah had time to protest.

THE golf club Easter ball was the main fundraising event of the year: a dinner, drinks, and dancing in the town's seventeenth-century manor house that was now owned by a large hotel chain.

Sarah had not been for the past four years. Pete had always compèred the auction, managing to squeeze as much money as possible from the wealthier of the guests. It wouldn't be the same without him. This year, however, the flowers had done something to her. Perhaps it wouldn't be the same without Pete, but it might just be fun.

At 7.30 p.m. Sarah was sitting on the edge of her sofa. Her make-up was subtle but reflected the light; her dress was perfect for the eating and dancing she was planning. A discreet pair of diamond studs flashed intermittently and a splash of floral perfume complemented both Sarah and the season.

By 7.45 p.m. Bev had not arrived. Sarah had rung her house but there had been no answer. She slouched back into the sofa. She could ring for a taxi, but that meant turning up alone, and she wasn't ready for that yet. Maybe Bev was stuck in traffic. Maybe there had been an accident. Maybe Bev had just forgotten. Sarah sighed; it looked like she wasn't going after all.

Then the doorbell rang. Sarah jumped up and straightened her dress whilst Bev shouted, "Sorry! Tights disaster!" through the letter-box.

In the hall, Sarah checked her make-up once more. She could hear Pete's voice in her mind, complimenting her. He'd always said she was a cracker and tonight she believed him.

Sarah smiled to herself before pausing to smell her daffodils, taking in their sweetness. She felt a rush of gratitude to whoever had sent them – Graham, Jim, even Alan. They had made her feel as vibrant as the yellow bouquet in front of her. Spring had not passed for good. ■

How Does Your Garden Grow?

by Ali McCulloch.

THE late summer sun warmed her back as Sandra bent, a little stiffly, over the flower-bed, working on her never-ending project of creating the perfect cottage garden. Since her retirement she'd really been able to devote some time to the plot and had filled the borders with tall mauve and dusty pink delphiniums, speckled foxgloves and violet lupins.

Wisteria covered almost one whole side of the thatched cottage and the long, purple flowers looked very elegant, draped as they were over the doorway. Her favourite flower, the old-fashioned scented rose, Wedding Day, scrambled through the apple tree that she'd planted with Bill not long after they moved in. She was proud of her garden and relished a sunny day collecting seeds and pulling weeds.

Sandra gazed over the much-loved plot and her eyes alighted on the old tyre swing hanging from the boughs of one of the trees. How fast they grow, she thought. Not the dandelions and cow parsley that threatened to overwhelm her borders, but her children. It seemed like only yesterday that Poppy and Heather were running wild across the lawn and paddling in the little stream at the bottom of the garden. How she missed the constant chatter that the girls had kept up, even as they crammed berries into their mouths and chased each other through the shrubs.

With a little effort, Sandra straightened up and walked along the thyme-scented path, past the lavender beds, towards the sun-bleached shed at the bottom of the garden. She opened the door and breathed in the earthy smell of compost and creosote, looking for her favourite beech-handled trowel. Casting her eye over the terracotta pots, carefully coiled hose and neatly labelled envelopes filled with seeds, she found the tool she was looking for. The wood was worn and smooth, but the blade was sharp and well maintained.

She still remembered walking, with her mother, down to McLean's to choose it. The ironmonger's had row upon row of tools meant for the mysterious world of adults. The trowel had been her first grown-up tool and Mr McLean had told her that if she looked after it, it would last a lifetime.

She could still make out her initials, *SW*, which her father had carved into the underside of the handle. When she ran her fingers over the letters, she had the clearest memory of Sandra Wilson, the girl she had been. She'd hoped that the girls would inherit her green fingers, but although they loved playing in the garden, they'd never developed Sandra's passion for making things grow.

Now Heather was a fully fledged career woman and Poppy was married to the lovely Martin, with Molly, a daughter of their own. Sandra's daydreaming was interrupted by the sound of voices out in the lane.

"Hello? Granny?"

The gate creaked on its hinges as Poppy and little Molly arrived. Sandra ushered them over to the well-padded chairs and tables set out in the shade

Illustration by Ruth Blair.

underneath the cherry tree. Poppy kicked off her shoes and wiggled her toes in the grass, and the little girl ran over to the swing.

Sandra soon fetched a clinking jug of lemonade and a tray of scones and biscuits. Poppy poured out juice for her and ladled jam on to a scone.

"Good jam, Mum," she said, savouring her first bite.

"Made from my very own raspberries," Sandra replied proudly, handing a plastic tumbler to Molly.

"Are there any left, Granny? Can we pick some?"

"Well," Sandra said, "let's see if we can find them after you've finished your lemonade."

A few moments later Sandra took Molly's fingers in her careworn hand and began a guided tour of the garden.

"What's that, Granny?" Molly asked, pointing to a plant in the herb garden.

Sandra crushed a leaf between her fingers.

"What does it smell like to you?"

"Mmm, sherbet lemons."

Sandra laughed.

"Well, yes, I suppose it is a bit. It's called lemon thyme. And what about this one?" She offered Molly a purple flower to smell.

"Mummy's favourite soap!" Molly exclaimed as she inhaled the lavender's summery scent.

Then Sandra picked a soft, furry leaf from a little bush.

"Close your eyes, Molly," she commanded gently, and began to recite a long-forgotten poem that her own mother had sung to her. "'Close your eyes and do not peek, and I'll rub spring across your cheek. Smooth as satin, soft and sleek, close your eyes and do not peek.'"

MOLLY squeezed her eyes tightly shut, a big smile on her face as Sandra gently rubbed the leaf across the little girl's cheek. Molly gasped and giggled.

"What was that, Granny? It's so soft!"

"Gardeners call it 'lambs' lugs', sweetheart, because it feels like the downy ears of baby lambs. Don't you think it feels like velvet?"

Molly was still rubbing the leaf back and forth across the back of her hand when something caught her eye.

"Look, Granny!" she said excitedly. "Look at that buzzy bee!"

"Oh, I can see him. Look, he's collecting pollen to make into honey."

"He's going right into that flower, he's almost disappeared!"

"He has, hasn't he? Do you know what that flower is called? It's a snapdragon. Look at the way the flower opens up to let the bee in.

"Sweetheart, why don't we see if we can find some nice flowers for your mummy to take home? Do you think she'd like these ones?" Sandra pointed to the sweet peas growing rampantly up a pretty pergola.

Gold Hill, Shaftesbury

SURELY one of the most picturesque views in England, Gold Hill in Shaftesbury will be for ever associated with the famous Seventies advertising campaign for a certain brand of bread, which showed a young boy gleefully freewheeling down the steep street on his bike.

The remains of the ancient Shaftesbury Abbey, built by King Alfred the Great, flank one side of the ancient cobbles, with the famous cottages on the other side. Gold Hill museum occupies the two cottages at the top of the hill, offering a glimpse into daily life in Shaftesbury in times gone by.

Beyond the cottages is the 14th century St Peter's church. Visitors who pause a while at this point will be treated to magnificent views over the Blackmore Vale.

"Oh, yes, Granny," Molly agreed. "She loves bright colours and they smell lovely."

"Do you know what's special about these sweet peas?" Sandra asked her.

"Special?" Molly asked, intrigued. "What do you mean?"

"Well, the more we pick, the more they'll grow back, so next time you come, there'll be even more flowers for us to pick."

Molly and Sandra picked a pretty posy, and the little girl soon had her arms full of the scented blooms as they turned a corner into the well-ordered vegetable patch.

"Let's see if we can find something to eat," Sandra said, casting her eye around the tidy plot. "Do you think we can find any strawberries?"

The pair crouched low beside the row of little bushes.

"Make sure you check under every last leaf, sweetheart," Sandra told her.

"I think I've found the biggest strawberry ever, Granny!" Molly proudly exclaimed, holding up a fat fruit. "Have you ever seen a bigger one?"

"Oh, not for a long time. That's a whopper. And what about the rasps?"

Sandra held the little girl up so that she could pick the choicest fruits from the top of the canes.

"What's this one?" Molly asked, pointing to a small straggly plant.

"It's called shepherd's purse," Sandra explained, showing Molly how the little heart-shaped seed pods opened up to show the tiny seeds inside, like coins in a purse. "It's a weed, though, and we need to pull it up. Pass me that trowel," she said, pointing to her favourite tool.

Molly picked up the trowel, carefully examining it before her little mouth opened wide in surprise.

"Look, Granny, it's made for me!"

Sandra looked at her quizzically.

"What do you mean, Molly?"

"Look here, Granny, on the handle. It's got my initials on it – *MS*." She held the tool out for Sandra to inspect and Sandra realised that, from Molly's point of view, the letters had been turned upside down. *SW* had become *MS*.

"What do you know? I think you might be right, Molly. I think that it may very well have been made for you." Sandra smiled.

SHE dug up the weed and threw it on to the compost heap and, as the afternoon sun dipped in the sky, the pair made their way back through the garden towards Poppy and the lemonade. Molly picked up a scone and Sandra gazed contentedly at her granddaughter's soil-covered fingers and berry-stained mouth.

She sat back and listened as Molly began telling Poppy about the colourful sweet peas and the scented herbs, and Sandra knew that she'd found a green-fingered gardener to inherit her skills and her beloved tools – her granddaughter, little Molly Samuels. ■

Driven To Distraction

LESLEY stood at the threshold of her daughter's bedroom and watched her dusting the computer screen. The room had never been so spotless. Lesley knew exactly what she was up to. Kayleigh gazed around, duster poised, looking for something else to polish. She nudged a CD into line in its rack before noticing Lesley.

"What do you think?" Kayleigh said, smiling proudly. "Tidy environment, tidy mind."

"It's fantastic. I'd completely forgotten your carpet was that colour."

Kayleigh ignored that.

"I think I deserve a break."

"Or," Lesley said, blocking the doorway and Kayleigh's path to the TV, "let's consider that your break. Since what you're supposed to be doing is . . ." She paused to check the timetable tacked above Kayleigh's desk.

Illustration by Corté.

by Camilla Kelly.

63

"Maths revision."

Kayleigh groaned. What she hadn't counted on when she'd spent the first morning of her exam leave painstakingly making a colour-coded timetable was that her mother would hold her to it.

"You're already half an hour behind. And before you say anything," Lesley continued, "the rabbits can wait to be fed. Your bedroom is tidy, your iPod is charged and your pencils are sharpened. No more excuses."

Kayleigh tapped her lips with a fingertip. Each nail of that hand was painted a different colour. Clearly she couldn't put anything away without reminding herself of its purpose first.

"Snacks," she said. "To keep up the flow of energy to my brain."

"I'll bring you something." Lesley pointed down to the carpet bar. "You're not to cross this doorway."

When she came back with Kayleigh's snack, her daughter was dutifully sitting at her desk, textbook open, cracking her knuckles. Lesley put the tea and biscuits down and kissed Kayleigh's forehead.

"It'll all be worth it."

"I know," Kayleigh said miserably. "But why did it have to be such a nice day?"

Sunlight fell across her desk in tantalising golden bands. Lesley gave Kayleigh's shoulder a sympathetic rub and left her to it.

SHE knew just what her daughter was going through. She remembered all too vividly the torture of exams that spread over the nicest weeks of early summer. In fact, she often felt a bit hypocritical insisting Kayleigh knuckle down when Lesley . . . well, Lesley hadn't. She'd been very easily distracted by all the things she'd rather have been doing, things that didn't require so much effort. As a result, she'd done poorly in her own exams.

After leaving school, Lesley had started an apprenticeship in office administration. She felt lucky now that she'd been given the opportunity to work her way up to office manager, but she couldn't help looking back with regret on what she might have achieved if she'd worked harder at school, and if she'd had more encouragement.

But the way she looked at it, she'd learned from her mistakes.

Kayleigh had sat through Lesley's lecture on the importance of making the best of your opportunities so often, bless her, she practically knew it backwards. Now wasn't the time to bring it up again. Now was just the time to provide tea and biscuits, and a little bit of peace and quiet.

Which, right then, meant doing something about Jamie.

Kayleigh's twelve-year-old brother was playing "Guitar Hero" very loudly on the games console in the living-room. The windows were practically rattling in their frames as he leapt about like something possessed.

"Muuum!" Kayleigh called irately from her room. "How am I supposed to concentrate on my maths with all that noise going on? It's too distracting! I can hardly hear myself think!"

In another minute, Lesley predicted, Kayleigh would be throwing down her pen and insisting on going for a long walk to clear her head. If only she would put as much effort into studying as she did into getting out of it!

Lesley pushed open the living-room door, flinching as the volume of noise hit her.

"Jamie," she shouted, catching her son mid-bounce. "How do you fancy earning some extra pocket money?"

Jamie paused his game and looked at her suspiciously. He knew better than to volunteer for anything before he had heard full details of exactly what it entailed.

"The vegetable patch needs weeding," Lesley said.

"How much are you offering?"

Lesley resisted the urge to tell him he should be outdoors anyway and after much negotiation they settled on a price. She turned off the TV and listened for any rumblings from Kayleigh's room. All was quiet.

That was a relief.

Easily distracted, it had always said on Kayleigh's school reports. Lesley could only suppose Kayleigh took after her that way. But it was much better – and kinder! – than the sort of thing Lesley's teachers used to write about her!

I N the kitchen, a pile of unwashed dishes waited in the sink, a pile of laundry waited next to the ironing board, and a pile of paperwork waited on the table.

Lesley checked the clock. She had a while yet before Ed would be home from work and she'd have to start thinking about what to make for dinner. If she managed to get all this done quickly, she might just find five minutes for herself.

She ploughed systematically through the housework. All was still quiet in Kayleigh's room, and through the window Lesley could see Jamie finish the weeding, tidy away the tools and then start a game of football with a neighbour.

After neatly filing the paperwork, she sat back for a moment. She checked the clock again. Yes, if she got a move on, she'd have quite a decent chunk of time . . .

"I'm starving," Kayleigh said, arriving in the doorway. She stretched her arms over her head. "Anything to eat?"

She opened the fridge and peered inside. Jamie, sweaty and tired, came in the back door, chatting to Ed, who set aside his car keys and gave Lesley a smile of greeting.

"Good day?" she asked him.

"Not bad. You?"

"Busy."

He gazed around at the tidy kitchen and the children bickering over who had had the last yoghurt.

"Come on, kids," he called. "We're going to get take-away for dinner. Jamie, go and wash first."

The children both hurried off to change, arguing now about what to have for dinner.

"THANKS," Lesley said, wrapping her arms around Ed's waist and giving him a squeeze.

"We might even stop at the park for a while. Does that give you enough time to do some reading?"

She was so grateful she gave him a kiss.

From a shelf under the bread bin, Lesley extracted her Open University coursework. She always kept it handy so she could draw it out in any spare moment.

"All day," she said, "I've been trying to get Kayleigh to take her revision seriously. I don't want her to make the same mistakes I did and still be trying to catch up twenty years later."

"But you are catching up, that's what's important."

She looked at her textbooks and sighed inwardly. She was daunted every time she saw the covers, she just couldn't help it. Business Studies. Hopefully when – if – she got these qualifications, her career would open up in more interesting ways. And she knew that once she settled down and began, her interest in the subject would soon take over.

It was just getting started . . .

"And with your natural management skills you're going to do brilliantly." Ed gestured to all corners of the house. "You've covered people management, time management and financial management all in one day. This course should be a piece of cake to someone with your experience!"

She smiled. Funny how quickly insecurity could be killed off if you were lucky enough to have someone who knew how.

The children returned, still arguing, and Ed hustled them out.

Quiet settled around Lesley. Perfect study conditions.

She laid the book out flat. Lifted her pencil. Hmm . . . could do with sharpening . . .

"Forgot something," Kayleigh said, dancing back into the room. She picked up the TV remote and slipped it into her pocket with a grin. "Don't want any distractions, do you? Remember: make the best of your opportunities while you have them."

"Yes," Lesley said fondly. "I remember. But thanks for reminding me." ■

Flipper

FLIPPER the Fabulous Dolphin has had a long career in film and television. Originally made into a film in 1963, the story of a young boy living in the Florida Keys who befriends an injured dolphin won the hearts of the viewing public straight away, and led to a TV series based on the same characters that ran for three years from 1964.

In the television series, Flipper was played by three dolphins, named Mitzi, Little Bit and Mr Gipper. Mitzi did the close-up shots, but as she wasn't particularly athletic, Little Bit and Mr Gipper did the stunt work. All three of them were trained by Milton Santini, a Corsican fisherman who became attached to dolphins after rescuing an injured one from his nets.

Milton set up the Santini Porpoise School in Florida in 1958, which in later years became the Dolphin Research Centre. The Centre continues its work helping injured or distressed marine mammals in the area, rescuing and rehabilitating them, as well as studying them, and is currently the only facility in the Florida Keys licensed to assist the area's population of manatees.

The show was revived in 1995 in the USA, before being remade in 1996, starring Paul Hogan, of "Crocodile Dundee" fame, and Elijah Wood.

After All These Years

by Sheila Norton.

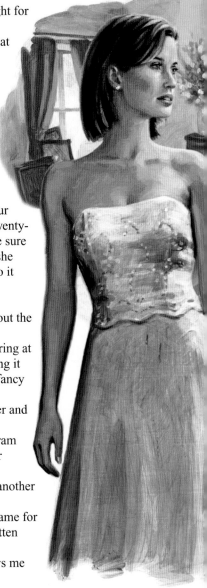

"**WOULD** blue be all right for your bridesmaid's dress?" Andrea grins at me. She knows perfectly well blue is my favourite colour.

"Lovely!" I give her a hug. "How many bridesmaids are you having?

"You're the only one, Jo. I'll be expecting you to run round in circles and organise everything. I hope that's all right?"

We both laugh. I don't need to answer. We've been best friends since our mothers met at the maternity hospital twenty-seven years ago. And I'm going to make sure her wedding to Tom is as wonderful as she deserves. In fact, I'm looking forward to it almost as much as she is!

We're out shopping for her dress the following week before I think to ask about the best man.

"A friend of Tom's," Andrea says, staring at a very flouncy white dress before flicking it along the rail dismissively. "Yuck. Too fancy for my taste."

"The dress or the best man?" I ask her and we both giggle.

"No, he's not fancy at all! Scott Bartram — he plays rugby with Tom. Remember him? He went to our school."

"Oh, him." I busy myself looking at another dress.

Scott Bartram! I haven't heard that name for years. But I'd be lying if I said I'd forgotten about him.

"What's that look for?" Andrea knows me

too well. "Wait a minute. I've just remembered — you went out with him, didn't you?"

"Only for a few weeks when we were fifteen," I say, shrugging dismissively. "No big deal. It just kind of fizzled out."

"Right," Andrea says, not sounding convinced. "It won't be awkward for you, will it? At the wedding, I mean?"

"No, of course not!" I reassure her.

What happened isn't important any more and I'd hate her to worry that there might be an atmosphere on her wedding day. I'll make sure there isn't. After all, I can be mature about this!

OVER the next few months I'm too busy at work, and with organising Andrea's hen weekend, to think too much about the best man. But as we get closer to the wedding in June, I start wondering what he's like now. Is he still as good looking? Then I remember how much he hurt me and I try, again, to concentrate on what really matters — my best friend, the bride, and making her day perfect.

By the time we go away for the hen weekend, I've almost succeeded in putting Scott out of my mind. But on the Saturday night, in a bar in Brighton, surrounded by a dozen of our friends from school and college, we have a couple of glasses of wine and one thing leads to another . . . When one of the other girls asks about the best man, Andrea nudges me teasingly.

"He's a friend of Tom's. But he used to be quite a good friend of Jo's, too!"

"Oh, really?" One of the girls chuckles. "Very good friends, were you, Jo?"

"Not at all! It was back in school, and we only went out on a few dates." The last thing I want is for everyone to be looking at me pointedly on Andrea's wedding day.

"Come on, Jo!" Andrea encourages me cheerfully. "It's a hen weekend —

Illustration by Richard Eraut.

we're supposed to share our deepest secrets!"

"Yes, come on — tell all!" the others are begging me.

"There's nothing to tell." I try to get out of it. "It was so long ago, it doesn't matter now."

"If it doesn't matter, why are you getting so flustered?" Andrea asked, as perceptive as ever.

"Because it was embarrassing. And hurtful. I felt too humiliated at the time to tell you what happened. And I've never really forgiven him!"

And then I finish my drink, and end up telling them the whole story, after all.

I WAS just a gawky schoolgirl, coming up to my fifteenth birthday. Scott was sixteen, in the year above us at school, and I thought he was wonderful. At the time, he lived round the corner from me, and we often got the same bus to school. And that was how it started.

We used to walk to the bus stop together, and although I felt quite shy in his company, we discovered we had the same taste in pop music and that helped to break the ice. I remember rushing into the classroom the day he asked me out and blurting it excitedly to Andrea.

"I'm going out with Scott Bartram! He's asked me to go to the cinema with him!"

"Cor, lucky you!" she said enviously. And then, as it was obviously the biggest concern for anyone of our age, "What are you going to wear?"

In the cinema he held my hand, sending me into an overdrive of anxiety that he might kiss me. I wanted him to, of course, but I had no idea what to do, and was worried he'd think I was hopeless. In the end, he didn't kiss me at all, but I'd spent the whole time panicking about it. When he asked me afterwards what I'd thought of the film, I was too embarrassed to admit I'd hardly even watched it!

"He won't ask me out again!" I wailed to Andrea the next day. "He must think I'm a total idiot!"

But, to my amazement, he did, and eventually we graduated from holding hands to the occasional, very tentative, awkward kiss. I worried endlessly that he'd soon tire of me, being so shy, and would move on to a more worldly wise girl of his own age. We didn't even talk much on our dates, but he was my first boyfriend, and I was the envy of the other girls in my class, so I didn't let on to them how silent and timid our awkward little relationship really was. In the solitude of my adolescent heart, I thought I was in love.

* * * *

A couple of weeks later, my parents told me about the special treat they'd arranged for my birthday — two tickets to a pop concert at Wembley. The group appearing was one of my favourites — and one of Scott's, too.

Ambushed!

THE walk was long and bracing,
   Through wind and stinging rain,
We marched along with purpose,
No time to feel the pain.
We knew each muddy footstep,
No matter just how grim,
Would trim those extra ounces,
Would make us lean and slim.
How toned would be our torsos,
How well-deserved our glow,
How slender, fit and healthy –
But what was that? Oh, no!
A cosy country café
Lay in wait to spell defeat,
Our downfall was hot chocolate,
But, oh, the end was sweet!
                    — *Maggie Ingall*.

"You can choose who to take with you," Mum said, giving me a conspiratorial smile. She knew Scott's mum and seemed quite happy about us going out together.

I couldn't wait to see him and tell him about the concert. It would be the most exciting thing ever — going to Wembley to see a live pop concert with Scott! But that same evening, with our next date not due for a couple of days, everything changed.

"Call for you," my mother told me, frowning in surprise as she handed me the phone. "It's Mrs Bartram."

I took the phone outside into the hallway for some privacy.

"Hello, Jo," Scott's mother said calmly. "Scott's asked me to call you."

My heart skipped a beat. Was she inviting me round for tea to meet the family?

"He wanted me to tell you," she went on, "that he doesn't really want to go out with you any more. Sorry, love, but you know what boys are like. He'd rather be with his mates, playing their computer games. I hope you don't mind."

Hoped I didn't mind? I felt myself going hot all over with the pain and mortification of it. He'd got his mum to dump me over the phone? He'd rather play computer games? What on earth was I supposed to say to that?

"Oh, OK, then," was all I could manage to squeak before putting down the phone and running upstairs to my bedroom.

"What did she want?" Mum called after me.

"Nothing!" I shouted back.

Wisely, she didn't pursue it. But, after I'd finished crying my eyes out, I somehow found a modicum of dignity from somewhere and decided, angrily, that I'd go to the concert with Andrea and enjoy it — and that I'd hate Scott Bartram for ever! I told Andrea the next day that Scott and I had decided not to go out any more and every morning thereafter I took the earlier bus to school just to avoid him.

* * * *

In the bar in Brighton, the girls are all gasping and exclaiming indignantly.

"Why didn't you tell me any of this at the time? Oh, Jo, poor you. He seems such a nice guy now!" Andrea says.

"Well, like I said, it was a long time ago."

"Even so!" one of our friends protests. "Being dumped by your boyfriend's mum — honestly!"

But, strangely enough, now that the story's out in the open, I realise I'm not really upset about it. In fact, saying it out loud, it actually sounds quite funny. We were only kids, after all, and just playing at going out together. Was my heart broken? Not a bit of it! I had a new boyfriend a few months later!

"Why are you laughing?" Andrea asks me, looking surprised.

"Well, you've got to see the funny side of it, haven't you? I mean, getting his mum to call me!"

We start to snigger, and before we know it, we're all collapsing in hysterics.

"He'd rather play computer games!" Andrea squeals. "That's hilarious!"

It's such a relief to be able to laugh about it. The anxiety's gone out of the situation. I'm quite looking forward to seeing him at the wedding now!

THE thirtieth of June is a beautiful sunny day — perfect weather for a wedding. I'm concentrating so much on looking after the bride that it's not till we're walking down the aisle of St Martin's Church that I remember about the best man. In the build-up to the wedding his name has been mentioned quite often and I've got used to the fact that we're going to come face to face in the very near future.

I thought I would see him at the rehearsal two nights before the big day, but he wasn't able to make it due to a work commitment. Or maybe he was still avoiding me all these years later!

As I catch sight of the back of his head now, I can't help grinning to myself. We eventually reach our seats in the front row and I take Andrea's bouquet from her and give her a final encouraging smile. She looks absolutely amazing.

As for Scott Bartram — he's very tall, with the same thick, dark hair I remember, and a rugby player's broad physique. When he turns to take his seat across the aisle from me, he catches my eye and we both blink as if we're surprised to see each other. Of course he's no more surprised than I am — he'll have been told many times that I'm the bridesmaid. I wonder whether he really does feel awkward about seeing me again? I chuckle to myself. It'll serve him right if he does!

When the service is over, when Andrea and Tom are officially Man and Wife, and I'm wiping away a tear as the final hymn ends, Scott holds out his arm and together we begin the walk back to the church door. The bells are ringing and everyone's smiling at the happy couple. I can already see people outside in the churchyard clutching their handfuls of organic confetti. It's nearly over; all those months of excitement and preparation gone in a flash. But it's been perfect.

A T the reception, I'm seated at the top table, between Andrea's dad and . . . the best man. Everyone's busy chatting, and it's not till we're on our main course that Scott turns to me.

"It's great to meet up with you again, Jo."

"You, too," I say, smiling at him. Yes, he's still just as gorgeous-looking as I remember!

"I've often thought about you, over the years."

"Really?"

"Yes, really." He puts down his fork, as if he's lost his appetite. "I was young and silly when we knew each other before."

"So was I," I admit. "Just a kid, really."

"But I was so immature." He raises his eyebrows. "Computer games! What on earth was I thinking of!"

I laugh.

"Well, I guess most teenage boys are obsessed with them . . ."

"But — preferring them to girls? To going out with you? I must have been mad!"

"Well, getting your mum to dump me didn't exactly win you any brownie points."

He puts his hand to his forehead.

"Oh, no. I had forgotten that. How embarrassing! You must have absolutely hated me!"

"I certainly never wanted to set eyes on you again, that's for sure!"

"Is that why you started getting an earlier bus to school?"

I blush a little and nod.

"I'm really sorry," he continues. "Have you ever been able to forgive me?"

I look back at him thoughtfully. I could tell him the truth — that being dumped in such a careless fashion hurt my fragile teenage pride terribly — or perhaps I can choose, right now, to put the past where it belongs.

"It's actually quite funny, isn't it? I mean, we were both so shy and self-conscious!"

The look of relief on his face is priceless.

"I used to be almost dumbstruck when I was with you. I really liked you, but I just found it all too difficult. I had no idea what to talk to you about."

"Me, neither. Apart from music!"

I FINISH my meal and sip my coffee while I listen to the wedding speeches. Scott's, in the usual tradition of the best man's speech, concentrates on Tom's past shortcomings and his luck in finding such a lovely bride. Everyone laughs in all the right places and I smile to myself. This adult version of Scott is sweet and funny. I really like him.

When the music starts, Tom gets up and leads Andrea on to the floor for their first dance. Everyone cheers and claps.

"We don't have to worry about tradition," Scott says. "If you'd prefer not to . . ."

"Don't you want to dance with me?" I respond lightly. My eyes hold his. Is he going to reject me — all over again?

"Of course I do," he replies at once.

We walk together on to the dance floor, he holds me close and we begin to move to the music.

"I'm so glad I've met you again," he says as we're dancing.

Andrea's smiling at me across the shoulder of her new husband. She's probably relieved that Scott and I have managed not to take a few swings at each other!

"I've always presumed you must have been whisked off by some lucky man long ago — you were so lovely. And still are, of course," he adds quietly.

"Oh!" I'm taken by surprise. "Thank you for that, I suppose. I haven't been whisked off by anyone yet, unfortunately."

"Then I hope it's not too late," he says, staring into my eyes, "for me to ask you out — second time around?"

I smile at him mischievously.

"Well, that would be very nice. But I have to warn you — if you mess me about, I'm going to have to get my mum to call you!"

We're doubled up with laughter as we walk back from the dance floor and Andrea gives me a questioning look. I wink at her and tell myself that she can wait till after her honeymoon to get the gossip.

Today's been all about my best friend and her wonderful wedding day. But I'm hoping the future, for me, might be all about the best man! ■

The Barn Dance

by Della Galton.

Illustration by Mark Viney.

SMALL stones crunched beneath their feet as they jogged at a brisk pace along the damp farm track.

"This is what my gran would have called a 'wow' day," Neil said.

"As in, 'Wow, I could have stayed in bed'?" Julie panted.

"No, as in 'Wow, isn't it beautiful!'" Neil stopped by a five-bar gate.

Julie stopped, too, more than grateful. She was beginning to think she wasn't a morning person. Correction, she *knew* she wasn't a morning person. This was all Siobhan Roberts's fault.

Gasping a lungful of air, she pretended to do up a shoe lace so Neil wouldn't

75

see quite how out of breath she was. But he was, luckily, otherwise engaged.

"Look." He gestured out at the stubble field which was draped in swathes of early mist. A swirl of crows landed and then took off again in perfect unison. "Isn't that a fantastic sight?"

"Mmm." Julie concentrated on getting her breath back.

He smiled at her. He hadn't even broken a sweat.

"Thanks for coming with me. I'm not going too fast for you, am I?"

"Not at all."

She had some vague recollection of telling him in the pub last night that she regularly worked out before breakfast. That would teach her to exaggerate. A brisk stroll round the park with Jacko, her rather podgy Dalmatian, wasn't the same as going running.

But Neil was such a nice guy, one of the nicest to join the sales team at Mack's Agricultural for ages. And last night he'd been paying rather too much attention to Siobhan Roberts, who'd been telling him all about the Moon Walk she'd just done for charity.

"Would you like to see the photos on my phone?" Siobhan had simpered.

Julie had decided drastic action was needed. Hence she and Neil were now charging around the country lanes at some unearthly hour when she'd usually have been snuggled in bed.

"Where's Jacko?" she asked, suddenly realising her dog wasn't in sight.

"Chasing rabbits further up the lane." Neil gave her another beaming smile and began to jog on the spot. "Let's catch him up, shall we?"

"YOU went running? You? Just to impress Neil?" Laura, who was one of her closest friends, and who worked in telesales, fell about laughing when Julie called into the office to get her appointments. "Don't you see enough of him already?"

"Not as much as I'd like. But I'm working on it. Anyway, it wasn't that bad. Actually, I'm not even sore." She flexed her leg and gave the toe of her boot an experimental twirl.

"You will be tomorrow. It's the day after it really gets you. That's going to look attractive — limping about at the staff barn dance."

"Oh, cripes, I'd forgotten all about that."

"You mean Neil's not taking you?"

"Er, I do seem to remember us discussing it a while back. Yes, I think he's taking me."

Laura narrowed her blue eyes.

"Hmm. Well, if he changes his mind, there's a group of us going by mini bus. I'd have mentioned it before but I thought you and Gorgeous Neil were already an item. Every time I see you you're bent over a clipboard, heads touching."

She pulled a face and Julie threw a pen at her.

"I'm getting him familiar with the area, that's all."

"Is that what you call it? He said he'd meet you at Shillingford Farm, by the way. He's running late. Car wouldn't start, apparently." She shrugged. "Are we still on for lunch tomorrow? We can compare notes on outfits."

That was something else she hadn't thought about, Julie mused as she drove to her first appointment. But that was partly because she didn't have a definite arrangement with Neil. He was so lovely that she'd been swallowed up in an uncharacteristic black hole of shyness. She couldn't act naturally around him any more. She was probably trying too hard, she decided glumly.

Neil had transferred over from the Longhurst branch three weeks ago and when he'd asked what there was to do around here Julie had mentioned the barn dance. He'd seemed keen enough, but the subject hadn't come up again and she didn't dare to raise it in case he said he was taking someone else.

She liked Neil too much, that was the trouble. OK, so she'd just discovered she didn't share his passion for early morning jogging, but they had an awful lot of other things in common. They'd both grown up in villages, they both sold farming implements for a living, they both liked dogs and they both preferred fish and chips to any other type of take-away. Gorgeous Neil was the most eligible man — as well as the nicest one — she'd met in ages.

"ARN dance?" Neil scratched his nose and looked troubled. "No, sorry, I don't remember you mentioning it. When is it again?"

"Tomorrow night."

"I've, er, arranged to go to the pictures tomorrow," Neil murmured.

"Well, that's no problem." Her voice sounded artificially bright. "Can't you change it? You can go to the pictures any old time."

"Yes, but I've arranged to go with someone." His attractive face went a dull brick red, and suddenly Julie knew the "someone" was female.

"Anyone I know?" There was no way of making that question sound casual.

Neil didn't answer.

* * * *

"Oh, Jules, I'm so sorry. I know you really liked him." Laura put a sympathetic arm around her shoulders.

It was Friday lunchtime and they were in the canteen, picking at salads because they were both on diets as usual. Neil had called in sick.

In some ways Julie was glad. It would have been awful driving around with him all day, knowing he'd be ensconced in the back row with Siobhan later on. He hadn't actually said he was going with Siobhan, certainly, but Julie was aware the other woman was avoiding her.

"Let's have a cake for afters," Laura suggested. "That'll cheer us up."

"I can't believe I went jogging for nothing," Julie commented as they queued up for their desserts.

"Two large pieces of your finest chocolate gateau," she said to Darren, the canteen manager. "Let's forget the diet."

"Coming up." Darren grinned at Julie. "You don't need to diet, anyway."

"He has a soft spot for you," Laura said as she carried the tray to a table on the far side of the room.

Laura sighed. Canteen Darren was nice enough. But he wasn't Neil, was he?

✳ ✳ ✳ ✳

The mini bus went through town on the way to the barn dance. Julie half thought she might spot Neil with Siobhan, queuing up outside the cinema. But there wasn't a queue. It obviously wasn't that popular a film.

"I didn't know she even had her eye on him," Laura said, when Julie mentioned it.

"I'm sorry. I'll shut up." Julie sighed. "I don't want to spoil tonight."

"Nothing's going to spoil tonight!" Laura held out her silver-striped nails. "We are going to have a whale of a time."

And, actually, they did. Neil would have been wasted at the barn dance anyway, Julie decided, because you didn't keep your partner longer than a few seconds. Laura had been right, she had felt stiff after the jogging. But all the marching, twirling and stepping soon sorted that out.

"This is probably doing me a lot more good than jogging!" she told her fifth partner of the night.

"You don't need to go jogging — slip of a girl like you." His voice was admiring.

"Who's the big guy in the tartan trousers?" she asked Laura when she sat down breathlessly at their table.

"Haven't a clue." Laura fanned her face. "Although he's with the lads from Nelson's farm. Maybe he's a new boy. Want me to find out?"

Julie shook her head.

"No, thank you. I'm off men."

"Attagirl. You don't need a man to enjoy yourself!"

"My sentiments exactly." Julie gulped a mouthful of wine. "Come on, they're about to start the next dance!"

IT had been extremely nice not to have to get up and go jogging the next morning, too, Julie thought, as she got ready to go to work on Monday. She and Jacko were back in their usual routine of twice round the park.

"Which is plenty of exercise, for us, isn't it, podge?" She chucked the Dalmatian under the chin and he wagged his spotty body ecstatically.

Julie was a bit anxious about meeting Neil at work as she drove in. She didn't want any awkwardness between them. Not when they had to drive

Melrose Abbey

THE peaceful appearance of beautiful Melrose Abbey in the Scottish Borders belies its turbulent past. The first Cistercian Abbey in Scotland, the Abbey was founded by David I in 1136 and dedicated to the Virgin Mary.

Freed from the feudal constraints that bound other institutions, it soon grew into one of the most productive centres in the area: by 1370 it had a flock of around 15,000 sheep – the largest of any religious house in the country – and around 22,000 acres of land. Such wealth attracted much unwelcome attention, and the Abbey was attacked and pillaged by various English monarchs. Robert the Bruce was instrumental in its restoration and, following his wishes, his heart was buried in the Abbey's precincts.

Now in the care of Historic Scotland, this beautiful site is well worth a visit – don't miss the carved bagpipe-playing pig hiding up on the roof!

79

around together all day.

He was waiting for her in the car park, perched on the bonnet of his car, his long suit-clad legs stretched out in front of him. He usually waited in the office, chatting to Laura. Maybe he was feeling awkward, too.

"I THINK I owe you an apology," he said, as soon as they were out on the road.

"I don't think you do." She glanced at his serious profile, feeling her hands tightening around the steering wheel. "I just got the wrong end of the stick. Did you have a good time at the pictures?"

"Er, no." He rubbed his nose. "I was ill, as it happened, that's why I didn't come to work on Friday. But I didn't realise the barn dance was such a big thing."

"Big thing?" She put a little casual question into her words. "What made you think that?"

"Laura," he said sheepishly. "She mentioned you were really looking forward to it. She had a bit of a dig at me for going to the pictures with Siobhan."

"I didn't know you were going with Siobhan."

"No, that's the thing. I wasn't going with her anyway. Look, I had a long-standing arrangement with an old friend who just happens to be female. She isn't a girlfriend or anything." He coughed awkwardly.

"Oh." Julie slowed down for the traffic lights which had just turned red, wondering if her face was the same colour.

"Look, is there any chance we can start again?"

"Start what again?"

"Em, us. This. We could maybe go out on a proper date?"

She was so surprised that she stalled the car just as the traffic lights turned green.

"If you wanted to. I mean . . ." He didn't sound a bit like his usual confident salesman self.

He touched her arm and she stalled the car again. The man in the car behind them honked his horn.

"Will it involve jogging?"

"No, it won't involve jogging." She could hear the smile in Neil's voice. "It might involve a drive out to a country pub where dogs are allowed. Then Jacko can come."

"Sounds lovely."

"We can sort out the finer details when you're not driving."

"Good idea," she said as she restarted the car for the second time and pulled away.

Laura had been right. You didn't need a man to enjoy yourself. But it was great to have the choice! ■

80

All Aboard!

by Celia K. Andrew.

THE red double-decker bus was parked behind a thick screen of tall pines that had protected it from the worst of the wind and the weather, clearly for some time.

"Wow!" Eleven-year-old Marcus, pausing in his demolition of the nettles and thistles, stared. Paula, nearly nine, bumped into him from behind and stepped around her brother.

"Wow," she repeated. Marcus hacked past the last few five-foot weeds and in awe the children approached the long-overdue bus to Croydon.

Grass had grown all around, but sheep had grazed it down and there was a worn track to the platform at the back of the bus. Marcus and Paula followed the path and climbed aboard. Old crispy pine needles and hay had settled in corners and there was a heaped mass of old coats in the luggage cubbyhole.

Paula scampered up on to one of the sideways seats and sat there swinging her legs and rubbing at the old polished leather, almost cracked through in

places. She slid down again and made her way to the front seats, sitting briefly first in the left and then the right, behind the driver's cab. She stood up to see better and looked at the big steering wheel and out of the front window into the clearing.

"Marcus, look, that's where the driver goes! We might be able to sit in his seat, too . . ." There was no reply.

Marcus hauled himself up the steep twist of stairs, using the thick grab-rail and marvelling at the height of

Illustration by Mandy Murray.

81

each rise. He paused at the top, looking down the length of the aisle, enchanted. He sat on the back seat by the emergency window and tried to push it open, but it wouldn't yield. Instead, he pressed the button to ring a bell, with no result.

DISAPPOINTED but not surprised, he walked along the cambered aisle between the seats, fingering the metal support poles and seat backs, unrusted, smooth, a pleasure to touch. At the front, he chose the window seat on the left and looked back to his hacked handiwork which had led him to this glade.

"Cool," he breathed. "Like something in a story. I wonder how it got here?"

He looked round, already imagining the top deck as his den for the summer holidays. His drum kit could live here and he could make as much noise as he liked: who would there be here to complain of the row? What if they could get the engine going? Dad might be able to drive the bus around – how cool would that be?

"But there's nobody to see us," he said aloud, remembering suddenly. "Everyone's back in Collier's Wood." For a moment, a flicker of sadness ran through him.

There would be a new school in the autumn; all his mates would be back at St George's without him. Nothing was ever going to be the same again . . .

"Ting, ting! Fares, please!" Paula was grinning inanely, pretending to take money from imaginary passengers as she progressed up the aisle. She was remembering some funny DVDs her dad had played them last Christmas – "On The Buses". The ticket-collector person had dinged the bell to make the bus go or stop and had said those words.

"Any more fares, please?"

"Mine!" Marcus joined in, content to humour her. "How much to Collier's Wood?"

"Last stop Croydon, young man," Paula said sternly. "You're on the wrong bus."

"I've got . . ." He scrabbled around in his jeans pocket. "Two pounds. How far will that take me?"

"To the treeline." Paula giggled. "You'll have to walk after that."

"We could make the bus go to anywhere we want," Marcus said, looking out of the window again, imagining the hills, far mountains, glens and rivers of their new country beyond the clearing. It had looked wild and alien on the journey up here in the car. A million miles from Collier's Wood.

"This bus won't be going back to Croydon," Paula said in a small voice, sitting down beside him and fiddling with her T-shirt sleeve. "It's in exile, like us."

There was a silence between them as each remembered the suburban life they'd left behind when their father had inherited this smallholding in the Highlands of Scotland.

"Whose do you think the bus is, Marcus?" Paula was turning her friendship bracelets over and over each other. One from Katey, one from Niddy, one from Susie . . .

"Don't know, but it's on our land, I'm pretty sure of that." Marcus rubbed a hand through his wiry dark hair. "Dad said it was Uncle Jonathan's – our – land right down to the road, and we haven't reached there yet."

"We could have my birthday party here!" Paula looked around, lit up again, imagining balloons and streamers and . . .

"I'll come to your party, Paulie," Marcus said, leaning forward and taking his younger sister in an unembarrassed hug. He knew just how she felt. He could feel her trembling a little and knew there would be tears any second. He wasn't really up to her crying.

"Let's go and look at the outside! Maybe we can get into the driver's door and sit by the controls!" He gave her a friendly shove and they wandered down the aisle together, touching the green-tinged leather and scuffing their trainers in the grooves of the wooden floor.

"If I set my drums up here . . ." Marcus paused by the longer rear seat and grinned. "I could bang and crash away and nobody would mind!"

"I could have the front as my travel agency." Paula turned back. "I could put up posters and stuff and Mum wouldn't shout at me for messing up the walls."

"Come on, Paulie, we'd better get back. Mum said one o'clock for lunch."

They clattered down the stairs again, and at the bottom, they both stood on the platform and looked round one last time.

"No neighbours to annoy here, anyway!"

"You can be the requests man at my party!" Paula laughed at him pretending to play his air guitar and drums.

"I'll have to get batteries, lots of them, for my CD player, then!" Marcus leapt off the platform and started running back along the path towards the hacked-open entrance to the clearing.

Paula stood a moment longer, before carefully letting herself down to the ground. She started running after her brother and wondered, briefly, why there was a path leading to the back of the bus in the first place . . .

WHERE'S my field-hook, Marcus? I need to get rid of some of the brambles by the gates." Their father eyed Marcus over his glasses at lunch.

"It's . . ." Marcus began and then stumbled. The hook was somewhere out near the bus to Croydon. "I'll get it for you straight after lunch."

"What on earth have you been doing, Marcus?" His mother put her fork down and stared at him. "You shouldn't be playing with sharp things like that."

"I wasn't playing, Mum. Dad's shown me how to use it. I was cutting back undergrowth and stuff, out in the fields."

"I hope you weren't swinging it near Paula – you might hurt her."

"Oh, Mum . . ."

"Kids do things like hack at brambles with machetes in the country, Jane. You'll have to get used to letting them off the leash a bit up here."

"He's dead good at it, Mum! We went exploring through the fields for miles. We haven't even reached the road yet!" Paula was bouncing a bit in her seat.

Easter

EASTER blessings touch our hearts
As spring wakes all around,
New life is filling field and tree
With colour, light and sound.
Easter blessings, yours and mine,
As once more earth revives,
But most of all, the precious love
Which comforts all our lives.

The Easter message gives us hope,
We know love cannot die,
We keep the knowledge life goes on
Though springtime passes by.
So share the healing and the joy,
It helps our spirit climb.
Go forward with a lighter heart,
Rejoice at Easter time!

— *Iris Hesselden.*

MARCUS wanted to keep the bus to Croydon a secret – Mum was almost bound to ban them playing on it if she knew. He glared a warning at his sister from the other side of the table. If he could have reached her with a quick kick, he would have done.

"We hacked through to this clearing in the jungle, and there's a red bus parked there, going to Croydon, and . . ." Paula stopped, her mouth still open.

She went very red and stared across at Marcus.

"A bus?" Their mother pounced on that.

"Well done, bigmouth," Marcus muttered as Paula went on. She'd given it away and she couldn't see the point in not sharing everything now.

"It's abandoned. It's a big red London bus, only it says it's going to Croydon."

"It was Uncle Jonathan's," their father put in. "He bought it when he retired from driving and then drove it all the way up here as a souvenir."

"Phil! You knew about it? A red bus on our land?"

"Well, of course I did. It's on what's left of the old wartime runway."

"Come and see it, Mum, you'll like it! Just like being back in London!" Paula was desperate for her mother to like the bus, because then she might not mind them playing on it and turning it into a drum studio and travel agency.

"Let's take a walk after lunch, love." Their father was also keen to get her to like the bus and everything about their new life here in Scotland. "If I remember from when I was a lad, the old runway isn't far."

"Well, all right, then. We haven't been for a walk together as a family

for years."

"Too long in London," their father muttered.

"You had a good job in London, and we had a nice flat."

"They didn't want me any more. We're better off with me up here with Uncle Jonathan's funny old farmhouse and my bit of IT work in Fort William and my nice fat redundancy cheque." He got up from his place and went round to hug her. "It'll be OK, love. Everything'll work out. Just give it time."

* * * *

The family wandered down through the fields, following the path Marcus had hacked out that morning. The July sun was gloriously warm in a part-clouded sky and unknown, unseen birds chattered and jabbered in the trees and long grasses.

"This is nice, love," Phil said, taking Jane's hand and squeezing it as they walked.

She smiled weakly, shrugged, swallowed a couple of times and wouldn't look at him.

"Great view of the loch from here, and the mountains."

"You can't make friends with a loch and a mountain."

"Oh, Jane, please try to like it. I'd feel better about the whole business if I knew you could be happy."

"But it's so lonely . . ." She swallowed again. "And the kids have no friends here."

"Not yet, but when they get to the school they'll make lots."

"We promised Paula she could have a party for her birthday. But there's nobody to invite . . ."

"LOOK, there it is!" Marcus pointed when they arrived at the edge of the clearing.

Paula was looking at something else.

"Look," she repeated. There was an old lady dressed in green sitting on the platform at the back of the vehicle, feet resting on the earth, and beside her a brindle greyhound lay, long nose on paws, watching the family approach.

It stood up slowly, and the old lady smiled across at them.

"Well, hello, there," she called, as though she owned the bus. "The Bishop told me you'd been here!"

"That's our bus," Paula said and her father shushed her bad manners.

"Public transport," the old lady said, getting to her feet and coming towards them. "Going to Croydon, I believe. How much is the fare, do you suppose?"

Her eyes were bright as topaz and her apple-round face was all smiles.

Paula's indignation abated at once. She grinned.

"About a thousand pounds." She giggled, falling in with the spirit of the banter.

"That's far too much. I think I'll stay here. Gently, now." The old lady spoke to the tall greyhound as he started towards the family.

"We're the McBrides." Paula's father held out his hand. "I'm Phil, my wife, Jane, and kids, Marcus and Paula."

"Jonathan said you'd be along one day. He was so glad to have someone to leave the old place to." She watched Paula hugging the tall greyhound. "And the Bishop was very excited when I arrived – he could smell you'd been in. He adores children, he'll be so pleased we have neighbours again."

"You're a neighbour?" Jane smiled tentatively.

"Sweetbriar Cottage, end of your track and along towards the village."

"Pleased to know you. Erm – ?"

"Peacock. Jeannie Peacock."

"I'd like a dog," Marcus said, pulling gently on the silky ears.

"We can have one now we don't live in Collier's Wood any more. Can't we, Dad?" Paula traced along the dog's backbone and ran her hands all down the long whippy tail. "He's just perfect. We could have one just like him."

"It's up to your mother. She'd be the one looking after it." He looked at his wife uncertainly.

JANE watched the children with the slim, handsome dog and bit her lip. After a second she said, "Well, it's something we can think about, certainly."

"Marc and I have thought," Paula said. "We love him."

"You can't have this dog, silly," Marcus muttered. "Just one like him, maybe."

"What were you doing just sitting on the platform anyway?" Paula looked at the sparkly old lady, thinking she looked a bit like a woodsprite in her green jacket and trousers.

"The Bishop and I love the bus. We come here often."

"What for?"

"To think. And to play my harmonica where it won't disturb anyone."

"You play the harmonica?" Marcus's mouth dropped open.

Jane McBride was feeling very strange. Sort of . . . going still inside, as though the churning and stirring of the past few months was being calmed

Skippy

ONE of Australia's best-known entertainment imports, "Skippy The Bush Kangaroo" started life as an Australian television series in 1966, telling the adventures of a young boy and his intelligent pet kangaroo in Waratah Park. Ninety-one episodes were made over its three-year life as a show. Although at the time of its screening Australian television was black and white, it was filmed in colour to help its chances abroad – it has been shown in the USA, Canada, Czechoslovakia and Mexico and is apparently still showing in Iran! Unfortunately, it was banned in Sweden as it was believed it would encourage children to think animals could do things they weren't actually capable of!

The rôle of Skippy was filled by three kangaroos — Jo-Jo, Stumpy and Wildy together with a few others that handled less demanding tasks. The executive producer had originally wanted the show to be called "Hoppy", but he was overruled by his co-producer!

Rex-Features.

87

down. She'd always loved going on the big red London buses as a child and the new versions just didn't have any character at all. And here was an original old bus, red and welcoming. She wanted to put out her hand and take hold of the vertical pole and pull herself up on to the platform and climb up the winding stairs and . . .

"You going to Croydon, Mum?" Paula scampered on to the platform behind her and followed her to the top deck.

JANE sat down on the very front seat and gazed out of the window. Paula sat on the seat opposite and just watched. Her mother's tight, tense shoulders dropped, she heaved a huge sigh and suddenly she turned to look at Paula.

"Let's not go to Croydon. Let's go to . . ."

"Neverland! Second star on the right and straight on till morning!" Paula giggled and leapt from her seat into her mother's arms. "Oh, Mum, it's just lovely. It's a real Big Red Bus and it's ours!"

"Someone else is coming to catch the bus," Mum said, indicating a boy and a girl of about ten wheeling their bicycles across the glade from the main road. The Bishop had raced to meet them.

"Kids!" Marcus exclaimed from behind his father.

"My grandchildren, Eddie and Caitlin," Mrs Peacock's voice came from behind him. "They'll be glad of your company these holidays. They've come to take me away home for some tea."

"Why don't you all come back to the house and have a cup with us instead? It'd be so nice to get to know you and hear all about the village. We've been feeling a bit . . . unattached to the world this past week," Jane said.

Her husband stared at her, first in surprise and then pleasure. He leaned over and hugged her.

"Yes, do come, Mrs Peacock. We've a party to discuss, and maybe you'll know where we can find a dog."

"My party," Paula squeaked. "Does Caitlin like chocolate cake?"

"Her favourite." Mrs Peacock smiled. "We'd love to come and take tea at the farm – it's been a while since I've been over." She nipped down the stairs to meet her grandchildren, nimble as a cat, and the family followed her.

"It'll be fun to share the bus," Paula said, eyes shining.

"I wonder if Eddie can play the drums?" Marcus asked.

"Do you think maybe a rescue greyhound, Phil? Or even two?" Jane wasn't even holding the rails as she descended the stairs.

"I think," Phil said, patting the last seat on the top deck, "that the bus to Croydon is the best thing that's happened to this family since we arrived in Scotland."

And he looked down at his happy, together family and their new friends and just knew everything was going to be all right after all. ■

Rainbow
On A Plate
by Kim Fleet.

THAT'S not red, it's orange," Callum complained, picking a piece of carrot from his plate. He waggled it at me, pinched between his thumb and finger.

"Almost red," I said, my heart sinking as he screwed up his face.

"Orange," he said stoutly. With his dark Celtic looks, black curly hair and blue eyes, he was the snap of his father, and my heart softened. His face said "Silly Mummy" as eloquently as only a five-year-old's can.

"OK, orange," I conceded, scraping the carrots from his plate on to mine. Callum happily turned back to his red dinner: tomatoes, beetroot and red pepper. This week, all his food had to be red. Fortunately I'd found some pork and tomato sausages at the butcher's, or it would have been tricky getting some protein into him. Callum insisted that beef was brown, not red.

"So what colour will it be next week?" I asked, praying he wouldn't

Illustration by Mandy Murray.

89

say "blue".

"Yellow," he announced.

Yellow? Good. That meant bananas, cheese, corn and squash were all possibilities. With a bit of luck I might persuade him that chicken was yellow, too.

Callum had started picky eating a few weeks before. I'd noticed that one day he only ate certain items from his plate and refused the others, stating, "They're not red. I only eat red food."

I'd shrugged it off, thinking it was a whim, but since then, he'd changed from only eating red food to only eating green, then brown, then orange, then back to red again.

"At least he eats a variety of things," my friend, Shona, herself a mother of three, said. "Mine would suddenly only eat sweetcorn, then just as suddenly only eat bananas. He'll grow out of it. Try not to worry too much."

My husband, Ian, agreed.

"He's probably copying some other kid at school. It's just a phase."

Easy for him to say. Actually, Ian was almost as bad. He couldn't have any food touching on his plate, and gravy had to be served separately altogether. No wonder Callum was a faddy eater. My heart sank as I watched the two of them at dinner: Ian with his food carefully separated on his plate, Callum refusing anything that wasn't the prescribed colour.

I'd been determined that Callum wouldn't be one of those children who were afraid to try something new. From the time he started eating solid food I'd always given him whatever Ian and I were having, and introduced him to a variety of flavours and textures.

I was surprised and pleased when Callum liked curry and prawns; less surprised when he rejected calamari and olives, but proud that he'd tried them. So when he suddenly stopped eating anything that wasn't the right colour, I worried. And as the weeks passed, my concerns grew.

"It'll pass," Shona reassured me. "Don't make too much of it and he'll soon be back to normal."

I took her advice and gritted my teeth when Callum pushed food round his plate, arguing it wasn't the right colour.

"GUESS what we did today at school?" he cried, a few days into the yellow regime.

"What's that?" I said, smiling at his flushed face and sparkling eyes.

"We planted sunflower seeds and we're having a competition to see who grows the tallest sunflower," he told me. "I'm going to grow one up to the moon."

"Fantastic! How did you plant the seeds?"

He told me in detail about digging the soil in the school garden, choosing a seed from the packet, placing it in the hole and carefully covering it over.

"And then we all got to use the watering can and water the seeds!" Callum said. "Mrs Picton's put a stick with our names on next to our seeds so we'll know who grows the tallest."

I was thrilled to see him so excited, and an idea unfurled in my mind.

"Would you like to grow some things at home?" I asked. "You could have a little patch of garden to plant what you liked."

"Could I? Yes, please, Mummy. Can we plant some seeds now?"

"Let's go and buy some seeds at the weekend," I said. "And we'll get you your own fork and trowel."

"And a watering can."

"And a watering can."

While Callum was at school the following day, I went to the nursery and checked out their seeds. Perfect, they had exactly what I needed.

O N Saturday, Callum and I studied the range of seeds and he bit his lip as he tried to decide what to grow.

"Hey, look, Callum. Purple carrots," I said, showing him the packet. "Carrots are orange," he argued.

"Not these ones. Look."

He clutched the packet in his small fist.

"Can we grow carrots, Mummy?"

"Of course. How about tomatoes? Or corn?"

"Look, Mummy. Giant onions. I could grow the biggest onion in the world."

"You could."

We selected a range of seeds, including purple carrots, miniature broccoli and giant onions, and went home to get busy planting. And watering. Some we put in pots outside, others we planted in a little patch of garden I'd marked out with stones and a flag as Callum's. The watering can was put to good use, then we sat back and waited for everything to sprout.

Every morning after breakfast, Callum scuttled into the garden to check on his seeds. I thought he'd burst with joy when the first green tips unfurled and poked through into the sunlight. Callum tended them carefully, weeding round the shoots as the weeks passed and the days grew warmer and brighter. After a couple of months, the peas were ready to harvest.

Unfortunately, it was a red week that week.

Callum and I snapped the pods from the stalks and drilled the peas into a bowl.

"Can I have these for my tea, Mummy?" he asked.

"They're green."

He frowned for a moment and popped a pea into his mouth.

"This week is red *and* green."

The peas were a great hit, as were the tomatoes, beans and mini broccoli.

A few weeks later the corn was ready, falling unfortunately in a green week. Callum stroked the brown beards on the end of the cobs and declared, "This week can be yellow and green."

As the harvest grew, he changed the rules time and again, eager to eat what he'd grown as soon as it was ready.

I sighed with relief at the rainbow of colours on Callum's plate, and was cheered by the sight of him eagerly clearing his whole dinner. It seemed the phase had passed.

Eventually the purple carrots were ready and Callum tugged them out of the soil with pride, and helped me wash the dirt off at the sink.

"How's your sunflower coming on?" I asked.

He frowned.

"Mrs Picton measured them today. My sunflower came second. William's was bigger by one centimetre."

"I'm sorry," I said, hugging him. "I know you tried hard. But second place is good."

"It's OK, Mummy," he said, and beamed at me. "Anyway, William hasn't grown purple carrots, like me."

I ruffled his hair.

"So what colour is it going to be next week?"

He considered for a moment.

"All colours, Mummy. Except blue." ■

Magic Trill

FLOWERS bloom profusely
In bed and border plot,
From urns and window-boxes,
Pewter troughs and pot,
Delphiniums and asters,
Stock and feverfew,
Hollyhocks and roses shine
Beneath a sky of blue.
Bright green the sheen of willows
Languid by the lake,
As regal swans go gliding by,
Cygnets in their wake.
All is fresh and beautiful,
I can never have my fill,
Especially when accompanied by
A blackbird's magic trill . . .
– Brian H. Gent.

Thinkstockphotos.

Dove Cottage

HOME to Lakeland poet William Wordsworth and his sister, Dorothy, from 1799 to 1808, Dove Cottage in Grasmere, with its then-uninterrupted view of Grasmere Lake and much of the valley, was a magnet for the great names of the Romantic movement. Visitors included Sir Walter Scott, Thomas de Quincy, and William's close friend, Samuel Taylor Coleridge.

Restored by the Wordsworth Trust and opened to the public from 1891, Dove Cottage today receives over 70,000 visitors annually, all keen to experience the site where the poet produced what are now regarded as his finest works. What trip to the Lakes would be complete without sight of this most inspiring of literary landmarks?

Rachel And The Butterfly

by Mary Kettlewell.

THE early June sunshine picked out the highlights in Rachel's long tresses. She walked through the grasses, skirt swishing. Insects buzzed, ants scurried and larks sang high in the sky. She was holding a bamboo-handled net and her blue eyes darted about, searching the flowers and hedgerows for butterflies.

Suddenly she stopped and stared intently at a clump of white-flowering hogweed, waves of excitement swirling up in her. She could not be mistaken.

The small brown butterfly had a row of orange spots on the upper side of the hind wing and an unmistakeable line of black spots round the edges. It was a black hairstreak, the extremely rare butterfly discovered by the Cambridgeshire entomological dealer, Mr Seaman, two years earlier in 1828.

She crept forward slowly and the butterfly soared into the air with a short, jerky flight and headed for a huddle of blackthorn at the edge of a copse.

She was so intent on tracking the specimen that she quite failed to see the notice in faded black lettering: *PRIVATE. TRESPASSERS WILL BE PROSECUTED.* She was twenty yards into the wood, peering here and there for the butterfly, when a voice from behind made her jump.

"This is private property."

She spun round to see a strongly built man in his early thirties. He was wearing a tweed jacket, breeches and a cap, and he carried a shooting stick folded up under his arm. His face was vaguely familiar, but she could not at first glance place him. Then it dawned on her. She had seen him at the village school open day some weeks previously when the headteacher had introduced him as a new governor.

"I'm sorry. I have just seen a black hairstreak. It is extremely rare and I was so eager to pursue it that I did not see the notice." Every inch of her being was longing to continue the search but he stood his ground.

"This copse is used for the breeding of pheasants. You are disturbing them."

His curt manner irritated her.

"I see no sign of pheasants here."

"That is because the breeding season is past."

94

"Then I cannot see that I am causing any harm."

He stared back at her.

"We are frequently troubled with vagrants here." He gestured brusquely back the way she had come. "There is a public right of way some hundred yards beyond the thicket."

"Rare butterflies tend not to keep to public rights of way," she said dryly. "Neither am I a vagrant." She lifted her chin proudly. "I am Doctor Fawcett's daughter."

At that he came off his high horse.

"I did not intend an insult."

Rachel had no wish to continue conversing with such a curmudgeonly fellow.

"I am glad to hear it. And now, sir, if you will step out of my way, I will remove myself from your land. Good day."

SHE was still fuming when she reached home. Her mother looked up from a piece of cross-stitch.

"You look to be in an ill temper, Rachel."

"I am, Mother. I had just seen a black hairstreak in the copse when an arrogant man ordered me off his land in a most disagreeable manner."

At that moment Dr Fawcett entered the drawing-room, having finished his morning surgery.

"Where were you, Rachel?"

"A mile or so outside the parish boundary, Father. On Hackshott Heath."

"It sounds as if you have met the Honourable James Lawne. He is a gentleman farmer new to the area. He has recently been made a school governor."

"Yes, I saw him at the school, but he is unfeeling and scarcely deserving of the title gentleman."

Her father nodded.

"He is rather terse, though I have only come across him a couple of times."

As soon as the doctor left, Rachel spoke to her mother.

"I'm going up there again. If there are black hairstreaks in that copse I want to see them."

"That might not be wise. You do not want another *contretemps* with him."

"I care not one jot for the Honourable James Lawne, Mother. If he does not appreciate rare butterflies then he is insensitive and boorish."

Mrs Fawcett knew better than to argue with her beloved daughter. She had the true characteristic of the redhead – a fiery temper.

In fact, James Lawne turned up at the doctor's afternoon surgery before Rachel set out. He presented with what could only be called a trivial injury.

He had nicked his finger and already the incision was healing. Dr Fawcett was no fool. He dabbed iodine on the cut.

"A long way to come for the physician, sir, with a minor complaint. Is there another reason for your visit?"

"I . . . er . . . met your daughter earlier in somewhat unfortunate circumstances."

"So I gather. She is a dedicated butterfly hunter and I understand that you were not pleased to find her on your land."

"That is so, and I would welcome the opportunity to put matters right with her."

The doctor smiled thinly.

"You will find her in the garden cutting roses. But as to what kind of reception you will get, I cannot say."

It turned out to be distinctly cold.

"MISS FAWCETT, I fear that I was unduly harsh earlier today in the copse."

She continued cutting roses as if less than interested.

"I cannot say that I found you amenable, sir."

"I will be frank. I had just come from a disputatious encounter with my handyman. He had not dealt with an infestation of moles as instructed and they had ruined my lawn. I was in poor temper."

"And the purpose of your visit, Mr Lawne?"

"Both to apologise and to say that you should feel free to enter the copse at any time."

One thing could be said of Rachel – she was not one to hold resentment.

"Your words are generous and I will certainly avail myself of your offer. The black hairstreak is exceptionally rare. It was only discovered two years ago."

"I seem to recall reading something about it in 'The Clarion'."

Mr Lawne had travelled three miles on horseback to make amends and Rachel felt that the least she could do was offer him hospitality.

"Would you care for tea and a slice of seed cake before you set off?"

"I would be delighted to join you." They sat down on a rustic seat and soon Bertha, the maid, brought them a tray. "Have you always been fascinated by butterflies, Miss Fawcett?"

"Ever since I was a little girl. Father used to take us to Wicken Fen. It is an area rich in beetles, birds, butterflies and wild animals."

"I can see the beauty of butterflies, but I confess that centipedes, slugs and the like are not to my taste."

She laughed.

"Nor to mine."

"Tell me, I feel uneasy at the thought of chloroforming the unfortunate creatures and impaling them on pins in showcases. Does this not distress you?"

"I don't do it, Mr Lawne. My interest lies entirely with observing the creatures."

"But you carry a net."

"I use it with great caution so that I can appreciate the colouring minutely. Then I release them."

"I am glad. I could not imagine you enjoying anything barbaric."

Rachel smiled.

"Thank you for the compliment. And what are your interests?"

"I enjoy farming and I would like to see the school curriculum expanded. The education of children is of the utmost importance."

Mr Lawne departed after tea with a warm smile, but not before taking note of Rachel's rich tresses of auburn hair, her blue eyes, full lips and soft skin.

Her mother was arranging flowers in the hall.

"I couldn't help noticing you and Mr Lawne through the window, my dear. Am I right in thinking that your disagreement has been settled?"

Rachel gave a casual toss of her head.

"Yes, he's not a bad fellow, Mother. A trifle hot-tempered, perhaps."

Mrs Fawcett smiled. It was a perfect description of her dear daughter.

THE next day Rachel put on thick shoes and a dress that would stand up to the rigours of brambles and thorns. As she drew near to the copse she saw, to her dismay, that a group of workmen had just finished erecting a palisade of high stakes round the area, completely barring all entry. She strode forward and addressed the foreman.

"What are you doing?"

The man looked up and gave a lopsided grin.

"Obeying Mr Lawne's orders, miss."

"But he told me only yesterday that I could visit the copse at any time."

"Not now you can't, lady. He specially told me not to let the doctor's daughter into the copse. That'll be you, miss."

She turned on her heel furiously. How dare he trick her? Was the man so cruel that he enjoyed playing foolish games? And she had been misguided enough to invite him for tea and cake.

Her father knew immediately that all was not well.

"What is troubling you, Rachel?"

"The Honourable James Lawne, Father. He has barricaded the copse. I am going straight to the Grange to confront him."

Her father was peering out of the window.

"That will not be necessary. He is just dismounting from his horse."

Rachel flounced out and did not mince her words.

"You have acted in a discourteous and heartless way, sir. You have dashed my hopes of seeing the black hairstreak and there is not a shred of decency in you."

Every Which Way But Loose

CLINT EASTWOOD'S smash-hit adventure comedy "Every Which Way But Loose" was an uncharacteristic and offbeat rôle for the actor. Eastwood plays the rôle of Philo Beddoe, a trucker and fighter roaming the American West in search of a lost love, accompanied by his friend and manager, Orville, and pet orang-utan, Clyde.

Clyde was played by an orang-utan named Manis, whose film credits also include "Going Ape!", playing "main monkey", and "The Cannonball Run". In between films, Manis returned to working with his trainers' act in Las Vegas. At one point during the filming, Manis grabbed Clint while he was driving a truck, worried as he could no longer see Clint's feet, hidden as they were under the car's dashboard. Manis had to be calmed down by talking to him over the radio.

Eastwood was full of praise for his co-actor, and was quoted as saying, "Clyde was one of the most natural actors I ever worked with! But you had to get him on the first take, because his boredom level was very limited."

Clint Eastwood was strongly advised against taking the rôle, but it ended up being one of his most successful films by far – and was second only to "Superman" in that year's box office rankings, despite receiving a panning from the critics.

He looked concerned.

"Miss Fawcett, you have completely –"

Rachel swept on regardless.

"To make matters worse it appears that you have ordered your men to exclude me personally."

She paused for breath and he took the opportunity.

"Mantraps, Miss Fawcett. That's why the palings have been put up."

She looked shocked to the core.

"Mantraps? But they have been illegal for all of two years. Surely you do not resort to such brutal methods to deter trespassers?"

"No, Miss Fawcett, I do not. My gamekeeper discovered an old and rusted mantrap in the copse last night. Had it sprung it would have done irreparable damage to his leg. I was terrified lest children and, above all, you, might enter the copse and come to unthinkable harm. The reason for my call this morning was to explain the situation."

Rachel blushed.

"Mr Lawne, I have done you a grievous wrong. I completely misunderstood the reason for the fencing. Will you forgive me?"

His reply made it clear to her that James Lawne was not the overbearing tyrant she had thought, but a man of generous heart.

"Of course I will."

He smiled.

"My gamekeeper thought that the *TRESPASSERS WILL BE PROSECUTED* notice was adequate. But not everybody observes the notice."

She blushed at his teasing.

"I thoroughly deserve that, Mr Lawne."

"A line of my men are going through the copse checking every inch of ground. Directly it is safe for you to revisit, I will let you know."

"That is most kind of you. Please stay for lunch. It is the least I can do after my rudeness and unwarranted accusations."

"I would love to do so, but I must hurry back to oversee the work. And do feel that you can call me James."

Rachel smiled.

"And do dispense with formalities as far as I am concerned. Rachel is my name."

"Rachel. A delightful name and full of such rich connotations."

HE climbed on to his horse and took the reins.

"A woman described in the Book of Genesis as being beautiful and lovely, I believe." He held her eyes for a long moment, until she flushed and turned away.

She returned late that morning with sketches of a mazarine blue under her arm to find her parents having lunch.

"A message arrived from Mr Lawne, my dear," her father said. "Apparently the copse where you sighted that rare butterfly is now safe."

Her mother helped her to a portion of pie.

"What a frightful business finding that mantrap. You could easily have been crippled by it, Rachel."

"I know. I was such a fool, Mother. I thought that James was behaving in an unpleasant way."

Her father looked up with a twinkle.

"I do not think it has done permanent damage to your relationship. He looked at you as he rode off with what one of our poets called 'a tender gaze'."

"Father," she said, blushing furiously. "I never heard such nonsense in all my life."

AFTER lunch Rachel took her butterfly net and walked along the track to the copse. As she passed the two large barns housing the livestock and the three haystacks close to the wood, she saw a tramp fast asleep, his boots sticking out from the covering of straw he had drawn over himself. It was a disappointing hour and the elusive black hairstreak did not emerge. When the sun disappeared behind a bank of cloud she decided to call it a day, as hairstreaks only fly in direct sunlight.

She took the path leading downwards and stared in horror. Where the tramp had been lying there was a ring of flames licking at the side of the stack. If the fire were to spread the barns and cattle would be engulfed.

She dashed into the cow byre, picked up a winnowing flail and began to beat at the fire. Soon her hands were black, her face speckled with ash.

At last the flames died down and she stepped back, exhausted, pale and shocked.

The sound of galloping hooves came to her ears and a voice called out.

"Rachel, my dear girl, are you hurt?"

She stumbled and would have fallen if James had not leapt from his horse and held her upright in his arms. When she had stopped trembling, he carefully lifted her up and sat her sideways on his horse. Slowly he led her back to the Grange.

"You have saved my barns, my cattle and stacks with your bravery, Rachel. I cannot thank you enough. But first we must ask my housekeeper to provide you with hot water and clean clothes."

An hour later she came down the stairs bathed and wearing a dress belonging to Mrs Hobbs. He looked at her anxiously or, to be more precise, tenderly.

"You have not been harmed in any way, Rachel? There are no burns on your hands?"

She smiled.

"Don't fret, James. I am perfectly well."

"I am so relieved. Now it is my turn to provide refreshments, and afterwards I will take you home in the pony and trap." He poured out the tea. "I am so grateful for all your help. I dread to think what would have happened if you had not put out the fire."

"I think I owe you a small favour, James, especially after the way I mistrusted you."

He passed her a slice of caraway seed cake.

"Something has been playing on my mind. At our first meeting I told you that my bad temper was due to my gamekeeper's incompetence. That was not the truth."

She laughed.

"Was it too much wine the night before?"

"Nothing like that. I had just returned from my brother's funeral in Ely and I was feeling upset. Hence my abrupt manner."

She put out her hand and touched his and it brought him comfort.

"James, what a tragedy. Surely he must have been only a young man?"

"It was a riding accident, Rachel. One of his great pleasures was to explore the countryside on horseback. He was a great lover of nature. Unfortunately his horse stumbled in a ditch and threw him headlong."

"You must miss him so much."

"We were very close. I feel as if a part of me has been lost."

"If there is anything I can do, please tell me, James."

"You have already done much, Rachel. I felt close to despair that first morning at the copse. But now I believe life to be worth living again." He

Smile!

WE all can make a difference
To someone's life each day.
A friendly smile, a word or two,
Will help them on their way.
Just to know that someone cares
Can brighten dull days, too,
And when you smile at someone else
They then smile back at you!
– *Joan Zambelli.*

Thinkstockphotos.

looked at her warmly. "Especially when I am in your company."

When Mrs Hobbs returned to remove the tray, she glanced at James and Rachel and nodded to herself. The master needed company and warmth after the loss of his brother. And if she wasn't mistaken, he had found it.

RACHEL, my dear, wherever have you been? And what is that dress you are wearing?"

"Fighting a haystack fire on James's land, Mother. I ended up covered in smuts and smoke and Mrs Hobbs kindly lent me one of her dresses."

"Good gracious, child, what will you be up to next? You are not harmed in any way?"

Rachel laughed.

"I do declare you think I am made of glass, Mother."

She absent-mindedly fiddled with the chrysanthemums in a vase on the sideboard.

"Poor James lost his brother in a dreadful riding accident recently."

"I am distressed to hear that. I hope you were able to offer him some comfort."

She looked down at her mother's embroidery, pretending to admire the delicate stitching.

"Mother, I feel strange inside. Warm and overflowing. I don't know what has come over me."

Her mother put an arm round her daughter and kissed her lightly on the forehead.

"But I do, my dear. You are falling in love."

Rachel lay awake all that night and slowly a plan formed in her mind. They had arranged to meet at the copse the following day and she excitedly told him of her thoughts.

"James, you said earlier that

one of your interests was to further education at the school."

"That is so, Rachel. I have racked my brains as to how it can best be done."

"I have an idea. Why not turn this copse into a reserve for birds, butterflies, flowers and other insects? The children are taught natural history, but the work is confined to drawing at their desks. It would be a wonderful place for them to see nature in all its variety."

In his enthusiasm James put his arm round her shoulder and she did not draw away.

"What a splendid idea. I would never have thought of it."

"There is more. Your brother was a lover of the countryside. The wood could be opened as a memorial to him. You could perhaps call it the Henry Lawne Nature Reserve."

She could see the dampness in his eyes.

"It is sweet of you to think of such a lovely plan. Will you help me to do it?"

"There could be no more delightful way of spending the time, James."

* * * *

The Henry Lawne Nature Reserve has been open for three months now and every day children wander through the bushes drawing beetles, birds, flowers and butterflies on their slates, exploring wildlife with their teacher.

One day in early July after the children had left James and Rachel were walking hand in hand by a clump of hogweed when she put a finger to her lips.

"Look," she whispered. "On that hogweed." A small butterfly with a row of orange spots round the upper side of the hind wing and a line of black dots was hovering on the flower. "It's the black hairstreak. We've found it at last."

It hovered for a few seconds then flew with its characteristic erratic, sweeping flight high up into the top of some sloe bushes and was lost to sight. As they gazed upwards he murmured in her ear.

"I am doubly fortunate, my dearest Rachel. Not only have I found the rare and shy black hairstreak. I have found something even more precious."

There in the wood, amongst hovering butterflies, the buzz of insects and the rustle of unseen creatures, he asked for her hand in marriage.

"Yes, James." She smiled. "But I must warn you that I am a redhead and redheads have fiery tempers."

"That is part of your charm. Even in anger you are beautiful." He kissed her again.

Later, when she had drawn breath, Rachel said softly, "Thank you, black hairstreak, for bringing us together."

And James echoed her words.

"Thank you, butterfly. Come back and visit us again next year." ▥

Sunderland

SITUATED at the mouth of the River Wear, Sunderland (from the Anglo-Saxon for "sundered land") was originally a small fishing village. Over the centuries it grew into a major port, trading coal and salt. Ship-building took place here from as long ago as the 14th century. As it grew, the city absorbed the neighbouring monastic settlements of Monkwearmouth on the north side of the river and Bishopswearmouth on the south bank.

Today, as a bustling, modern city with the peace of Roker beach and rolling countryside only minutes away, Sunderland is well worth a visit.

Something Lost

by Kay Seeley.

I WATCHED the young couple walking down the street, their arms around each other. She gazed lovingly into his eyes and he gave her a squeeze. That used to be us, I thought, my Steve and me. I sighed. "There's something missing. I'm not sure what it is, but I want it back," I said. I was with my friend, Ginny, in the coffee shop in town for our regular weekly gripe and moan session, putting the world to rights.

"When we were first married, Steve never left me without giving me a kiss. He bought me flowers every week and held my hand in the street – so proud he was to be seen with me." I took a sip of coffee and grimaced. "Nowadays I might as well be invisible. It's as if the closeness has gone, drowned in a sea of worries, children and growing old."

Ginny sipped her coffee.

"You can't expect love's young bloom to last for ever," she said. "My Barry spends all his time in the shed and he talks to the plants in the greenhouse more than he talks to me. Men – who'd have 'em?"

Well, me, I thought. I would. I sighed.

"I know. Steve's lovely and I wouldn't swap him for the world, but I wish he'd be a bit more attentive. Sometimes I feel like a piece of furniture that's been there so long you stop noticing it."

Ginny gazed at me and smiled.

"I know what you mean. When I first married Barry, we were so close I knew what he was thinking. I could finish a sentence before he said it. Now . . ." She shrugged.

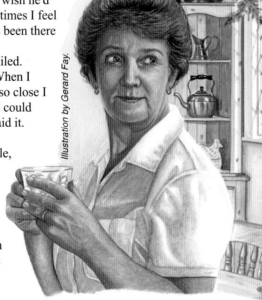

Illustration by Gerard Fay.

We sat in silence for a while, pondering over our coffee.

"What about a weekend break?" she said, brightening up. "Book a nice hotel somewhere romantic and spring it on him as a surprise. That should put the sparkle back."

106

I thought about it and warmed to the idea; then reality set in. I shook my head.

"There's nothing I'd like better," I said. "A posh hotel, waited on hand and foot, pampered and fussed over, but Steve would hate it. His idea of a great weekend is camping out on a riverbank, spending all day fishing and all evening in the pub watching football. No, it's no good unless it's something we'd both enjoy. It would cost a fortune and Steve would say it's a waste of money."

Ginny sighed.

"Barry would never leave his tomatoes at this time of year and he'd fret if he couldn't water his beans every day. I'd never be able to drag him away from the allotment, either, so I understand the problem."

The following week, sitting in the same coffee shop in town, Ginny produced a magazine from her eco-friendly bag-for-life.

"Look at this," she said, shoving it in my face.

A full-page spread featured a glamorous model in a soft-focus pose. It read, *Unleash your inner glamour and take a walk on the wild side*, then it went on to promise that, with their expert guidance, anyone could look a million dollars. Experienced stylists offered hair, make-up, manicure and fashion advice to turn the most ordinary into something exotic and enthralling, the whole experience culminating in a photo session with a professional photographer including one free photo. Who could resist, I thought.

I took a deep breath. If I looked half as good as the model, it would certainly make Steve sit up and take notice. But would I dare?

"I don't know what to say," I said eventually to Ginny.

"It's easy," she said. "Say yes. What could it hurt?"

"Apart from the fifty quid?"

"There's a special offer – two for the price of one. It's your birthday soon, so why don't we do it as a birthday treat?" The grin on her face spread from ear to ear. "Come on! It'll be fun and you did want to re-ignite that spark."

Ginny was right. I deserved a treat, so we booked it.

The girl on the telephone asked what kind of look we were aiming for.

"Something guaranteed to knock our husbands' socks off," Ginny said.

The girl laughed and suggested we find pictures of what we had in mind and they'd do their best to match it.

The next day Ginny came over and we spent the afternoon drinking tea and going through my stack of magazines, putting aside the tantalising recipes and the "How to lose two stones and still eat chocolate" articles, and each chose a picture of our preferred rôle model. I chose Meryl Streep in "Mamma Mia" and Ginny chose Cheryl Cole.

"We might as well make it as challenging as we can," she said, laughing.

The brochure said to bring a selection of outfits and accessories, so the day before the session Ginny brought her stuff round, I turned out my wardrobe, jewellery box and accessories drawer and we spent a hilarious afternoon choosing our outfits. It reminded me of diving into the dressing-up box when we were kids and the fun we used to have. At least that's one thing we haven't lost, I thought, our sense of humour.

The first item I tried on was the suit I had worn to my daughter's summer wedding.

Ginny shook her head.

"That's Ladies' Day at Ascot," she said. "We're looking for night-time in Paris."

I giggled. I didn't have anything that remotely resembled a night out in Paris.

"I'm aiming to stun with simple sophistication," I said. "Not knock Steve unconscious with a front row seat at the Folies Bergère."

Ginny insisted we'd need bright colours for dramatic effect, so back went my beiges, camels and pastels and out came my sparkly evening outfits; anything shimmery, low cut or revealing.

The biggest surprise was Ginny's midnight-blue Grecian top with its softly draped neckline edged with silver, which highlighted the creaminess of my skin. The colour brought out the sapphire in my eyes. I tried it on more in fun than expectation, but it looked fabulous. It was definitely a winner.

Then I looked out a white silk camisole to wear under my crimson velvet jacket and a deep purple top that I'd bought on a mad impulse in the sales and never worn. I also threw in my staple little black dress for good measure, a long black skirt and some evening trousers.

GINNY looked fantastic in my shimmery, bottle-green dress, the colour reflecting the emerald in her eyes. She added a couple of her dressier numbers for luck. We paraded up and down in front of the mirror like a couple of teenagers let loose in a clothing store. If nothing else, we had a lot of fun.

Accessories were easier. I had an unbelievable array of scarves, ranging

108

from discreet to gaudy, and had no problem picking some out.

We spent three hours going through my jewellery boxes, trying everything on. I discovered things hidden at the bottom of the box that hadn't seen the light of day for years. Things I'd forgotten about – some of it quite beautiful – and I wondered why I never wore them any more.

Changes in my lifestyle, I guessed, but I vowed to wear the gorgeous pieces I'd gathered over the years as often as I could from then on. Every piece brought back a precious memory. Rooting through my jewellery was an enjoyable pastime, but it didn't bring us any nearer to deciding what to take.

All afternoon, trying on the outfits, I tried to cultivate an air of mysterious aloofness, and by the time Ginny left, I'd perfected my femme fatale impression, but I couldn't help chuckling every time I thought about it.

※　※　※　※

The day of the session dawned bright and clear. The freshness of the perfect spring day boded well. Flowers bursting into bloom and new life sprouting from the trees felt like a good omen as we caught the train to town.

The salon was luxurious. I felt a little overawed, but Ginny barged right in. The receptionist was charming, took our coats and ushered us into a dimly lit room with soft music playing for our "personal consultations", which included complimentary champagne.

The day went so quickly I can hardly recall the details, although I do remember the feeling of indulgence. I also recall sinking back in a massage chair to have my hair shampooed. A most peculiar feeling at first, but I soon came to enjoy it and I was sorry when it stopped.

I asked Raoul, the hairstylist, who looked about fifteen, "How long have you been doing this sort of thing?"

"About eighteen years," he said. "I've worked all over the world, once on a cruise ship and on a film set. This is the best, though, helping beautiful women make the most of themselves." He was so nice that I relaxed as he snipped, brushed, highlighted, curled, teased, and sprayed my thatch.

"It won't be too short, will it?" I asked at one point as he snipped away.

"Trust me, you'll look fabulous," he said and brought me another glass of champagne. So I trusted him, sat back and sipped champagne, while he snipped, brushed and sprayed some more.

Ginny had copper highlights put in her rich chestnut hair, which curled softly around her face.

"Great hair," I said when her stylist had finished. "Shame about the face."

We both collapsed in champagne-fuelled laughter as we made our way through to the make-up room.

"What's that stuff they use to fill in the cracks on the wall?" Ginny asked. "We could do with a bucket-load in here." I managed to stifle a fit of giggles.

The girl in make-up was lovely and so dedicated I allowed her free rein to practise her artistry on my face. She smoothed, patted and painted.

"Lavender eye-shadow and blusher to bring out your eyes," she said. I nodded and smiled. By the end of the session, I had enough make-up on to plaster the living-room wall.

"Of course, it has to be thick for the photo," Ginny said as she posed this way and that in the mirror next to me. "You wouldn't put this much on at home."

Next stop was the manicurist. After my nails were filed and buffed, I chose a pale pink varnish. The young girl shook her head. She selected a deep plum polish. I swallowed back my comment about dark colours showing the chips, reminding myself that models don't have to worry about chipped nail varnish. They don't have to wash up, either, I thought. Ginny chose vivid scarlet.

The last thing was the photographer. We had our pictures taken separately and together in various positions, from lounging languidly on a chaise-longue to leaning forward provocatively on a fur-covered bench, pouting into the camera. There was even one of me giving come-hither looks while swinging in a flower-bedecked hammock. I almost fell out and had Ginny creasing up with laughter. Not one of my finest moments. I hadn't had so much fun in ages and the time flew by faster than an express train.

THERE was a special viewing room for us to see the photos. I think I had expected more of a transformation, and the photographer noticed my disappointment.

"What's wrong?" he asked.

"I thought I'd look fabulous," I said, "but I've still got eye-bags and more wrinkles than a ten-year-old russet apple."

He laughed. Then he did something magical with his mouse and the eye-bags, wrinkles and sagging jaw-line all disappeared.

"Now do it for real!" Ginny said.

One consolation was that Ginny still looked like Ginny, only done up like a dog's dinner. Cheryl Cole had nothing to worry about.

We each chose our free photo and bought one of the two of us together as a souvenir.

On the way home, I gazed in wonderment at my photo.

"If only," I said. "If only I looked like that. Still, I've had a great time and it's been an experience I'll never forget."

"Me, neither," Ginny said. "I wonder what Steve will say when he meets us at the station."

Steve! I'd quite forgotten the reason for our day out.

"I bet he doesn't even notice," I said, coming rapidly back to earth.

"Of course he will. You wait, he'll be amazed."

I wished I could believe it.

By the time we arrived at the station it had started to rain, a light drizzle that sank my spirits even further. I stood in the station, looking glum.

"I don't have an umbrella," I said. "My hair will flop and my make-up will run and I'll look such a fright that Steve will think I've escaped from a Hallowe'en horror movie."

"You're an old worrywart. It won't be like that at all."

Then I saw Steve running along the pavement. He ran up to Ginny.

"Come on, quick," he said. "I'm parked on a double yellow." He looked right past me.

Ginny hesitated. Steve did a double take.

"What have you done to my Izzie?" he said, looking straight at me. "Where is she?"

"It's me," I said. "The new and improved Izzie, glamorous and alluring." I fluttered my newly extended eyelashes.

His face crumpled.

"There was nowt wrong with t'old Izzie," he said in his gruffest Yorkshire tone. A frown creased his brow. My heart sank faster than a rock in quicksand.

"I liked the old model," he said. Then a sly smile spread across his face and a twinkle lit up his amber eyes. He rubbed his hands together. "Still," he said, "a change might be fun."

The look in his eye told me all I needed to know. Excitement fizzed through me like bubbles in champagne. I felt the old loving spark between us that I'd missed for so long. It wasn't lost after all. ■

Evening's Spell

THE sun sinks soft behind the trees
As stealthy steals the night,
Owls and bats have taken flight
And early stars are shining bright
Whilst gently blows the soft warm breeze.

The spell of evening now is spun,
Where dappled shadows merge,
Little creatures then emerge,
Exploring every leafy verge,
In homage to the day now done.
– *Brian H. Gent.*

Thinkstockphotos.

The Sweetest Thing

by Angela Pickering.

MAGGIE surveyed the mouth-watering spread of home-made sweets on her stall. She'd made quite a few of them herself: fondants in orange and lemon with sugared fruits on top, green and white mints and her favourite chocolate truffles, all displayed in sets of four in mousse pots and covered with plastic wrap.

Her mouth watered slightly at the sight of them, but then she considered the number she'd accidentally eaten whilst making them. I might be giving you up, she thought, looking at the truffles.

She smiled. Her daughter had come up with the lovely idea that Maggie should join the playgroup fund-raising committee. Not all of Sonia's ideas for improving Maggie's life had been so welcome over the years, but she had to agree that this one had been a cracker.

"They're always looking for help and it'd do you good, Mum. You spend far too much time on your own these days," Sonia had said. Maggie had been forced to agree.

"Hmm," she said with a sigh. "Now that I've retired, I do miss the company."

She'd left her job at the supermarket a couple of months earlier, but had started to wonder if it had been a mistake.

"You didn't have to retire," Sonia pointed out. "You could have stayed on for a few more years."

"I know," Maggie said, "but women of my generation always expected to retire at sixty. So I did."

Sonia chuckled and gave her mum a quick hug.

"You are silly, Mum." The hug tightened. "But I do love you."

Maggie's eyes prickled suddenly. There were moments when Sonia was so like her dad that Maggie felt his loss as if it had been yesterday instead of years before.

"I'll have some of the chocolates, please," a customer said, dragging Maggie back to the present.

She handed a pot over with pride. She almost forgot to take the money for

112

them, she was so excited. The playgroup won't make much profit from the fête at this rate, she thought, and resolved to be more careful.

Something snagged the leg of her trousers and she glanced down. She jumped with horrified surprise when she found herself starring into the huge blue eyes of a blonde-haired toddler who was holding on to her leg.

"Hello," she said at last. "Who are you? Where's your mummy?"

"Nana," the child said, giving her the most amazing grin. "Nana tweets."

"Tweets, yes," Maggie replied, still scanning the small crowd that milled about the field.

"Nana," the baby cried again and lifted chubby arms to her. "Nana."

Maggie threw caution aside and succumbed to the age-old appeal of a baby and gathered the little one up into her arms.

"Where's your mummy?" she repeated, although not expecting an answer.

The little blonde head snuggled into her neck. She bounced the child on her hip as if it were only yesterday she'd held her own babies. The baby held on to the strands of Maggie's hair that had escaped her white chef's hat.

"Faye," a deep voice cried from somewhere in the field, and a grey-haired man came puffing up to the stall. "Oh, thank goodness I've found you." There

Illustration by Jim Dewar.

113

was a hint of tears in the voice, and Maggie felt a stir of pity.

"She's all right," she said. "She's fine."

"Dan-dan," Faye said, lifting her head from Maggie's shoulder and reaching out for him. As the baby was taken from her arms, Maggie felt the loss of the warm body almost like a pain.

O H, thank you so much," the man said. "I thought I'd lost her." He frowned and smiled at the same time at the little one, as if he couldn't decide which expression was more appropriate. "The little scamp climbed out of her pushchair over there. I should have strapped her in, but I never imagined she'd do something like that. It's the first time I've looked after her by myself."

Maggie could see that he was shaking a little.

"It's all right," she said. "We've all had moments like that."

"My daughter would never have forgiven me if something had happened. I'd never have forgiven myself. I only took my eye off her for a second." He took a deep shuddering breath and clung to the baby as if she were the only thing keeping him on his feet.

"She's fine. Really," Maggie said, and, to distract him, she held out a truffle. "Have a truffle."

"Tweets," Faye said.

"I'm Maggie." Her heart was full of sympathy for him. "I'm due a break in a minute; let me buy you a coffee. You look like you could do with one."

The man smiled properly at last.

"David," he said through a mouthful of truffle. "But you can call me Dan. That's what Faye calls me since she can't say Grandad yet. I rather like it."

"She called me Nana," Maggie said. "I probably remind her of your wife." Nothing if not subtle, she thought, wondering at her own sudden boldness.

"Oh, no, Faye never knew her. My wife died years ago. Faye calls all . . ." He paused.

". . . old ladies Nana," Maggie finished for him. She laughed at the blush that spread over his face, feeling a matching one creep up her own cheeks.

"Sorry," he said. "No, not that. It's your hair. She likes ladies with silver hair." He looked down. "As do I," he muttered.

Maggie's heart was suddenly doing cartwheels. She hadn't felt like this in years. Someone cleared their throat loudly and Maggie realised that she'd been ignoring her duties as sweet-seller. There was a little queue forming and she moved to serve, although her hands were trembling ever so slightly.

She lost track of Dan and Faye as she sold her confections, until at last Sonia arrived to take over for a while.

"Well done, Mum," she said. "You've sold loads."

"I know," Maggie said. "We've made lots of money for the playgroup. Especially if all the other stalls have made as much as we have."

114

"I expect they have. I made a good bit on the ball-pond. That was a great idea for the toddlers." Sonia grimaced. "Except for that one chap whose little girl lost her nappy in the pond and he had to go in to fish it out.

"He was rather nice, though, Mum, about your age," Sonia said. "I had a little chat with him after and I . . ." She paused, gazing at the heavy bag of coins Maggie had thrust into her arms. "Wow, that's loads. Well done, you."

Another queue had formed by this time, and the conversation ceased under a rush of fondants and truffles. Maggie was deflated, too, when the hand-over to Sonia was complete, for she could see no sign of her two new friends. She gave herself a mental shake. It was a nice idea, she thought, but obviously not for me.

She decided to have a look round the fête and then have that coffee. Waving her fingers at Sonia, she set off in the vague direction of the ball-pond.

"Nana, Nana!"

Maggie recognised the voice. Dan was bumping a pushchair over the grass towards her, and Faye was delighting in the ride.

"Maggie," he called. "Wait for us. You owe me a coffee."

He arrived at her side, out of breath.

"I'd have waited at the stall for you, but Faye was a bit too interested in the sweets. I couldn't have resisted her much longer."

"Isn't she allowed sweets?"

"Well, not the amount she'd like. I'd already bought her a candy floss."

" I know." Maggie touched the side of her neck. "I'm wearing some."

"You're also still wearing your chef's hat," he said. "It suits you."

＊　＊　＊　＊

Later, over coffee while the gorgeous Faye slept in her pushchair, Maggie was hard-pressed to decide which one of them she liked the best. But when Dan invited her for dinner and touched the back of her hand softly, she made a snap decision.

"I'd love to," she said, breathless.

"I must thank the young lady at the ball-pond," he said, his smile matching hers.

"What for?"

"Well, she sent me over to the sweet stall; that's where I was heading when Faye made her great escape attempt. She said I'd find something there that Faye and I might like."

"Tweets?"

Dan laughed.

"There's something I have to tell you, though," he said, blushing again. "I can't stand chocolate."

"That's all right," Maggie said, picturing him with his mouth full of truffle. "I might be giving it up myself." ▥

A Trouble Shared

by Rose Paterson.

MARK HARRIS wondered if his guitar had always been this heavy or if he was just out of condition. His arm ached from carrying it in its hard, moulded plastic case the quarter of a mile from where the bus had dropped him off. But he couldn't have left it at home; when he met up with his two friends at the music festival, they almost always had a jam at the end of the day.

Mark, Jake and Sean had been nineteen when they met at uni and had formed a band, fully convinced that it was only a matter of time before their unique talent was discovered.

He smiled at the memory. Well, they were all grown up now, and those dreams of stardom had fallen away as – ever so gradually, it seemed to him now – they had evolved into responsible, hard-working husbands and fathers.

But these two days of freedom meant a lot to them. Within minutes of meeting, the years peeled away, and they found the core of their friendship intact, despite following very different paths.

They weren't all that great at keeping in touch: just the odd text or e-mail with news of any import. Life happened, things changed – but the two days' festival gig was written in stone.

Playing together, rusty as they inevitably were, brought back those carefree years, and then they went back to their everyday lives renewed and restored, ready to face the prospect of beckoning middle age with wry equanimity.

Mark rubbed his shoulder for a minute then re-adjusted the straps of his rucksack. He didn't have too far to go now to the festival site, and he'd been glad to escape the cramped bus. He sucked in big, deep lungfuls of fresh country air as he marched happily along the grass verge, enjoying the sensation of stretching his legs.

The sun was beating down and the back of his neck was starting to prickle, despite his thick dark hair (greying at the temples now!) His

116

Specials

soup of the day
tomato and basil
—
steak pie served
chips or potato
choice of veg
—
rhubarb tart and cus
or
choc fudge

ation by
Dixon.

stomach growled. A wide, red awning signposted a café about a hundred metres ahead.

* * * *

The waitress brought him a mozzarella cheese and ham panini, a small glass of beer and a smile that reminded him of his auntie Rita.

Mark glanced around. One or two people were intent only on eating their lunch, but a few were watching a young lad standing just outside the entrance.

He'd propped open his guitar case and was singing fearlessly what sounded like his own songs. He had a good voice, and Mark liked the way he played his guitar, with love and respect and more than the basic technical skill.

A few people were dropping coins and change into his case, for which he gave a brief nod. Auntie Rita's auburn-haired lookalike whisked by once or twice, speaking to Mark out of the side of her mouth.

"We should really move him on, but I'm a bit worried. He's been here a couple of days. Makes a wee pile of money, and he'll only take the odd glass of lemonade on the house.

"I wonder where he's staying . . . I'm beginning to think he might be a runaway."

Mark had been thinking the same thing; the boy was slightly built and perhaps small for his age, but he didn't look much older than fifteen. He was clean but his clothes looked wrinkled and slept in.

The waitress asked Mark to speak to the boy.

"You have a kind face, son, and you're a musician, too. I somehow get the feeling people trust you, and you listened when I told you my boring life story!"

Mark had guessed Joyce was carrying a heavy burden despite her cheery, too-bright smile. It hadn't taken much to draw her out.

"You'll see your grandchildren again, Joyce," he'd assured her, taking her hand. "I know it's a cliché, but time really does heal all wounds."

He hoped he'd helped her to feel better.

CHARLIE. An' I'm not goin' back! I'm finished with school. I just wanna play music. It's my life, man."

The boy was sitting beside Mark and after a discussion about the greatest living acoustic guitarists, Mark had asked his name and why he was here, busking, instead of being at school.

It turned out to be the same old story; Mum had remarried and he didn't get along with his new stepdad.

"Why not give it a chance, Charlie?" Mark was saying, watching as the boy wolfed down a plate of glistening, golden chips liberally doused in

Born Free

THE uplifting true story of couple Joy and George Adamson was made into a film in 1966, starring Virginia McKenna and Bill Travers. It tells of how the couple raised an orphaned lion club, Elsa, to adulthood, and eventually returned her to the Kenyan wilds.

For many, the real stars of the show were the lions who played Elsa. The real Elsa was raised alongside two other cubs with the Adamsons. The other two cubs were sent to Rotterdam Zoo and Elsa remained. After facing an ultimatum from their boss when Elsa was accused of causing an elephant stampede through a village, the Adamsons had to choose whether to send her to a zoo or rehabilitate her to the wild. After much hard work in developing her natural skills, Elsa was eventually released.

Elsa went on to have three cubs, who were much more averse to human contact than Elsa, so much so that very little is known of what became of them in the years after Elsa passed away.

Making the film became a life-changing experience for actors McKenna and real-life husband Travers, who then went on to become animal rights activists and were instrumental in creating the Born Free Foundation, a prominent international wildlife charity that devotes itself to "keeping wildlife in the wild".

tomato ketchup. "Everyone's adjusting. It's not easy when parents split and then meet someone else . . ."

"He's right, love. You just listen to him." Joyce skirted by, refilling their glasses en route to the other tables.

Charlie had finished his meal and was strapping on his guitar again, apparently in preparation for another "set" outside the café, but Mark was still worried the boy might bolt. Then his mobile rang. He listened for a moment before speaking.

"Not long, no. Just stopped off for a bite to eat. Yeah, go ahead and see a couple of bands, pitch the tent, don't worry about waiting for me . . . Hey, what are slaves for!" He laughed, then stowed his mobile back inside his shirt pocket.

WHEN Charlie stopped for another break, Joyce brought huge chocolate doughnuts and they talked some more.

"Looks a bit like Mum." Charlie jabbed his chin towards Joyce's retreating back.

Mark nodded.

"It's funny . . . when you're away from home, on holiday or something, you'll often think you see a loved one. Guess that means you miss them. Or you turn around and for a few seconds the place you're in reminds you of a street in your own home town."

"I do miss her . . ." Charlie blinked back a tear and turned his head away to hide it.

"Go back home, then, buddy," Mark said gently. "For a while yet, anyway. I bet they'll be glad to see you.

"You've got real talent, Charlie. Work on that and one day you could be headlining this festival! And even if you don't, you'll still be happy doing what you love, right?

"Now . . . want to borrow my phone?"

Joyce was nodding in approval.

Charlie looked from one to the other and shrugged.

"Maybe . . ."

*   *   *   *

"So how was it, getting away from it all?" Mark's wife asked when he got home the following night.

"Well, I was a tad late, but the festival was great once I finally got there. We still rock."

"Whoever would think you crazy young guys were now . . ." she counted off the fingers on her hand ". . . a teacher, a lawyer and . . ."

Mark grinned as he slid his dog collar around his neck.

"A shepherd?" ▓

120

A Shoulder To Cry On

ANGELA beckoned me to her desk and handed me a file. "This is in your neck of the woods, Karen," she said with a smile. "I've had a young chap on the phone who would like to buy a recently built flat or house near the centre of town. He's moving back from the city soon and he's only got a couple of days off work. Perhaps you could show him round these few on your estate."

Our small estate agency had handled most of the work on the little development where I'd recently bought a house. Now some of the other properties had come up for sale again and we were handling the business.

"He'll arrive about two-ish so get an early lunch," my boss said with a smile. "It'll give you a chance to vet some new neighbours."

by
Christine Evans.

Illustration by André Leonard.

121

I glanced at the name. *Duncan Price*. It looked familiar, but I couldn't place it.

I knew him immediately when he came in the office, though. Duncan Price, the handsomest prefect in school. He'd certainly been the best looking, but also the most arrogant and bossy.

The other girls in my class had drooled over him, but Marnie, my best friend, and I couldn't stand him, especially as he gave us detention for something trivial — at least I'm sure it must have been trivial. I couldn't wait to tell her!

We shook hands as Angela introduced us. I didn't enlighten him that we'd met before.

"I'll leave you in Karen's capable hands," Angela said. "She lives on the Lakes estate, which I'm sure will be perfect for you. It's near town and very convenient for the amenities . . . and schools."

"I . . . er . . . don't have kids," he said. "I'm not married."

"Well, if ever you did . . ." Angela gave me a grin.

MY boss was an inveterate matchmaker. She'd been trying to fix me up with someone ever since I'd joined the firm. If only she knew how much I'd disliked her newest client.

But he was pleasant enough now, full of the charm (or should I say smarm) that he'd shown in our school days. I'd never been the recipient back then, but he'd had a regular fanclub of sixth-formers hanging on to his every word. Marnie and I were a couple of years younger and beneath his notice.

I drove him to the estate, chatting pleasantly.

"There are a couple of houses on Windermere Drive to show you," I told him. "And a flat on Rudyard Avenue."

"Oh, I see; the roads are called after lakes."

"That's right. I live on Thirlmere. It's quite a nice little estate, new build, of course, on what used to be the paint factory."

"Oh, I remember that," he said. "My dad was in charge of quality control."

He was quiet for a while as I told him a little about the properties. He didn't seem to be listening, but I rabbited on all the same. We pulled up outside the first house: a two-bedroomed semi with a neat garden.

"I didn't expect to be moving back home," he said thoughtfully. "But my mother's ill and Dad's finding it hard to cope. I hope to help out a bit.

"I could move in with my parents, but Mum would try to look after me and she isn't up to it at the moment. I don't think your parents ever really think you've grown up, no matter how old you are."

"I'm so sorry," I said, taken aback that he sounded so humble and unlike his old arrogant self.

He gave me a thoughtful smile.

"But you don't want to hear about my troubles. Let's go and see what's on offer."

Reluctantly, I found myself warming towards him and resolved to do my best for him.

THE nearest property was a flat. It had originally been bought as an investment and was plain and soulless.

"You could make something of this," I suggested. "It's a blank canvas to fill with your own taste."

He stared out of the window.

"I've gone off the idea of a flat," he said. "I've just lived in one and now I'd like a bit of garden to sit out in."

"Then come and have a look at the house at the end of Windermere Drive," I said.

I had been hoping to avoid that property, as the garden of the house actually backed on to mine. But, of course, he was delighted with it as soon as he saw it.

The house felt warm and welcoming. A harassed young mother, who was also very pregnant, showed us around her home.

"We need something a bit bigger," she explained. "We're looking at another place on the estate. It's a very friendly place and so convenient for town — oh, and schools."

"Well, that's a good sign that you still want to stay on the estate," Duncan said, patting the curly head of a small boy.

"Have you got a family?" she asked.

"No, I'm not married," my client said, looking embarrassed that people kept asking him.

"Of course, you'd need to redecorate this room. I expect Thomas the Tank Engine isn't a cool look for a bachelor pad," the young mum said with a giggle as we inspected the nursery. "Unless, of course, you've got a partner."

"No. No," Duncan said in a tone I couldn't quite understand.

Did he sound bitter? Was it sadness — or even exasperation? I expected he'd forgotten how nosy people in our small town could be.

She offered us tea, but I explained we had a few more places to see.

"It's a bit more expensive than I'd planned," Duncan said, enthusiastically examining the kitchen. "But it feels right."

We went to see a couple more properties, but he was keen on the house on Windermere Drive.

"I think I'll put in an offer," he said. "Whew, I could do with that cup of tea now."

We were passing my home.

"That's where I live," I said. "Would you like to have a cup of tea while we're here and we can go through some of the paperwork? You can see the house from here."

"That'd be great," he said.

S O that's how I came to have my least-favourite school prefect in my house. He was the perfect guest, though, and praised what I'd done with my home. Then I told him that we'd been at school at the same time, though he didn't recognise me, of course. He'd handed out so many detentions that I was just another name in the black mark book! I was still itching to tell Marnie.

We shook hands formally.

"So we'll be neighbours when all the paperwork is sorted out," he said. "Thanks for showing me round."

I'm sure he wasn't quite as handsome as he'd been at school. His once-long blond hair had darkened and was short. His previously smooth skin was fashionably whiskery and his eyes had lost their arrogance, too. Now he wore an intangible air of sadness. But he was still very attractive, much to my discomfort.

* * * *

Angela was thrilled with me.

"Congratulations, Karen, selling the house and a nice, handsome neighbour for you, too," she said.

"I'm definitely not interested," I said. "I was at school with him."

"Oh, was he a spotty nerd?"

"No, not at all. He was the best-looking lad in school — and he knew it! He was a pain and he gave me and Marnie detention."

Angela chuckled.

"Methinks she doth protest too much!" she joked.

* * * *

"Duncan Price going to be your neighbour — lucky you!" Marnie said when she called round with a bottle of wine for a girls' night in.

"I thought you couldn't stand him?" I said in surprise.

"Oh, well . . ." She chuckled. "You know how it is. You have to act cool, don't you? Not that he was ever interested in us fourth years. Still, he was a dish."

I was rapidly becoming disillusioned these days, what with Duncan Price acting humble, and now Marnie confessing to a secret crush on him.

"I'll have to introduce you to him," I said.

"Might prove interesting," she said with a glint in her eye.

But Duncan wasn't going to be interested in either of us — unless it was on the rebound. He confessed as much when he came to the office the next day and asked me out for coffee.

124

Norfolk, Horsey Wind Pump

THE closest Broadland village to the coast, Horsey boasts a magnificent windpump on the banks of a dyke leading to Horsey Mere. One of a series of drainage windmills used in the Norfolk Broads to reclaim the land to allow it to be used for agriculture, the Horsey windpump was active until 1943 when it was hit by lightning.

Since then the Grade II listed building has been restored by the National Trust and is open to the public on certain days for visitors to enjoy not only a trip back in time, but also a superb view over the village from the top of the five-storey structure!

"Feels much more friendly than talking in the office," he said. "I'd like to thank you for all the work you've done. I should get the mortgage by the end of the week."

It was as we sipped our coffee and indulged in a lemon bun that he mentioned his girlfriend — or should I say ex-girlfriend.

"These were Ramona's favourites," he said thoughtfully, toying with the sticky cake. "But she doesn't want to know me now I'm moving back home. I thought she was special but . . ."

He looked so sad. He took a deep breath and changed the subject.

"Can you confirm the list of furniture the sellers are leaving?"

I lost my chance to commiserate with him. I don't even know if he'd have welcomed it.

It must have been one of the few times he'd been dumped, though he'd left plenty of broken hearts in his wake. I might have felt it served him right, but I didn't.

EVERYTHING went through smoothly. I noticed Duncan fitting blinds some weeks later and waved to him across our gardens. Then he called over the fence as I was mowing the lawn.

"The weather's been so nice I was thinking of having a barbecue as a house-warming. Would you come?"

"That'd be great," I said and offered to make some salads.

"Thanks — and bring some friends, too."

I definitely had Marnie in mind.

She'd pulled out all the stops when she arrived.

"You know it's a barbecue?" I said. "Will you be all right on the grass in those heels?"

"Of course," she said with a grin.

Duncan recognised Marnie straight away, which wasn't surprising with her flaming red hair.

"I know you. You asked me to write in your autograph book when I left," he said, handing her a glass of wine.

I gave her such a look!

"Honestly, Marnie!" I said.

"It was worth a try," she said, chuckling.

But the barbecue was great fun. We knew lots of people from school and the town.

Marnie made a beeline for a boy who'd been in our class.

"I thought you fancied Duncan," I said.

"Not after what you told me. I don't want to be his shoulder to cry on, thank you very much. I've just rediscovered Todd and, actually, he's a lot of fun."

I noticed she'd taken her shoes off and was walking barefoot.

"Enjoying yourself?" Duncan asked, appearing beside me. He'd finally cooked his way through all the chops, burgers and sausages.

"It's really good," I told him. "I knew I'd done the right thing selling you this house."

I'm sure he had just been about to say something nice when a stunning blonde stepped through the French windows.

"Ramona!" Duncan said.

He was rooted to the spot. His look was intense, but I couldn't tell what he was thinking.

"Hi, Duncan," she said casually, flicking her hair. "I didn't expect you to have company."

"Welcome to my house-warming. These are all my friends — past and present," he said, smiling at me.

"I . . . er . . . came to talk to you privately," she said with a determined look on her face.

"But not now," Duncan said with an equally steely glare. "Have a glass of wine."

She shook her head.

"I see you've settled in nicely. So you're determined to stay?"

"You haven't come to persuade me otherwise, have you?" he asked in surprise. "I did ask you to come with me."

"Yes, but surely . . ."

She glanced at us as if we were a bunch of uncivilised yokels. It was obvious she'd been confident that she'd persuade him to go back with her. Suddenly she seemed uncertain.

"Are you staying or going?" Duncan asked a little abruptly.

She hardly hesitated.

"There doesn't seem much point in staying," she said angrily.

He didn't even see her to the door. Then he became the life and soul of the party.

WHEN almost everyone had left I found him out in the garden.

"Do you want any help clearing up?" I asked.

He raised his eyes to me and I could see he'd been upset.

"She hurt me so much," he said quietly, "and she's quite oblivious. I never realised before how self-centred she was."

He'd been as bad himself once, but time and life had changed him. I touched his arm in sympathy and he gave me a sad little smile that touched my heart.

"Thanks. You're a good friend."

So do I want to be a shoulder to cry on? Time will tell. We're good friends for now, but deep down I hope we'll become more. That's one secret I'll keep from Marnie. ∎

Keeping Afloat

by Mary Ferris.

KEN and I have done nothing but argue lately." Jenny sighed, taking the mug of tea Pat held out to her. "We even had a row this morning before he went to work. I don't know what to do." Jenny had called round to see her friend, hoping to catch her before she started her shift at the local supermarket, and they were sitting in Pat's cosy kitchen. Jenny stared absently at a vase of freshly cut flowers in the centre of the table as she wiped her eyes with her handkerchief.

"I always thought that Ken and I were rock solid." She sniffed.

"Don't be silly — of course you're rock solid," Pat replied robustly. "You can't expect to be married for twenty-three years and not have a bad patch or two."

"Twenty-four years," Jenny corrected tearfully. "It's our silver anniversary next year." She took a deep breath to steady herself. It was all she could do not to start sobbing. "We've had fallings out before, of course we have. It's just that there have been so many recently."

Pat looked at her thoughtfully, the swish of the dishwasher the only sound for a moment.

"I think I know what the problem is," she announced.

"You do?" Jenny's fingers tightened on the handle of her mug. "Really?"

"Yep. You're suffering from empty-nest syndrome. I was reading about it the other day. I don't know about it personally, of course, never having had children, but apparently it's very common. A woman spends years making a home for her family, then the children fly the nest and she's left feeling empty and worthless. You see?"

Jenny did see. She nodded glumly. It was exactly how she was feeling. It had been bad enough when Adrian, their first-born, had moved to London to be near his girlfriend, but since the twins had left for university the previous autumn, home just hadn't seemed the same any more.

"That's only half the problem, though."

"Oh. You mean Ken?"

Illustration by L. Antico.

Jenny nodded.

"He hasn't been himself for months — for the past year, if I'm honest. Oh, Pat, what if he's having an affair?"

Pat burst out laughing.

"Your Ken? Having an affair? Don't give me that," she said. "He's potty about you, and always has been."

"I hope so, Pat, I really do. But there hasn't been much affection between us lately."

"I expect that's because you've each been caught up in your own problems." She paused. "How's his work going?"

"Well, he doesn't say much, but I know orders have fallen off this past year."

Ken owned a small building company in the local town, specialising in outdoor rooms, as his ads put it.

"The recession's hit a lot of businesses. I suppose if you're planning a conservatory, it's going to be one of the first things you put on hold in difficult times."

"There you are then, that explains it." Pat nodded. She glanced at the clock on the dresser and pushed back her chair. "Give him a bit of slack, and everything will work out, you'll see."

"If you say so," Jenny said, draining her mug before getting up, too.

"You've got too much time on your hands now that the boys have gone," Pat told her.

Jenny had to admit it was true. She thought of all the committees she used to sit on, the fund-raising events she'd helped to organise, and the ferrying to and from after-school clubs and activities. And that wasn't to mention the hours she'd spent in the kitchen feeding the boys and their hungry friends!

"Have you thought about getting a job?" Pat asked.

"A job? Me?"

She laughed.

"Of course, you!" She came over and put her arm around her friend. "Why not? I'd go round the twist without mine."

Jenny's mind went back to the time before the boys had come along, when she'd worked at the local garage as a secretary-cum-girl-Friday. That had been the last proper job she'd had. She'd thoroughly enjoyed it, she admitted, but so many things had changed since then.

"Who'd have me?" She grimaced. "Everything's computers these days. I can send an e-mail, thanks to the boys, but spreadsheets and things?" She shook her head. "I'd be useless."

AFTER dropping Pat off at the supermarket, Jenny found herself driving around aimlessly, the day stretching out emptily before her. The washing was done and hung on the line, the vegetables prepared for their evening meal, the carpets were vacuumed and there wasn't a speck of dust anywhere.

Pat was right. She'd have to have something to fill her time. But what?

Finding herself on the road out of town heading south, she decided to stay on it. She'd go to Sandy Cliffs, the little stretch of coast where they'd had such happy times when the boys were little. Even when they'd grown older and had their own interests, it had still remained her and Ken's favourite place. As he often said, it was a place you could clear your head and think.

She drove through the countryside, the sun glinting on greening fields. She inched down the window, and the haunting sound of birdsong came through the air. It was as if it was trying to cheer her up with its hope of better days to come, she thought, managing a smile.

Lassie

ERIC KNIGHT'S fictional collie, Lassie, first appeared in his novel "Lassie Come Home", the story of a rough collie's trek over many miles to be reunited with the boy she loves. Published in 1940, the novel was filmed by MGM in 1943 starring the dog Pal, who then went on to appear in six other films.

Pal was never intended to be the star of the show, hired instead as a stunt dog, but after the lead collie refused to enter the overflowing San Joaquin river for a dramatic sequence, Pal stepped in and so impressed the director that he was immediately hired to take over the lead rôle.

After the film, Pal's owner and trainer, Rudd Weatherwax, then went on to buy the Lassie name and trademark from MGM, and spent some time touring rodeos, fairs and similar events across America in the early Fifties. In 1954, the long-running and Emmy-award-winning television series, "Lassie", started, and over the next nineteen years a succession of Pal's descendants appeared on the show.

A recent 2005 remake of the film starring Peter O'Toole featured an eight-year-old Lassie the ninth, a direct descendant of Pal. This dog was trained by Carol Riggins, who had been a co-trainer of dogs with Robert Weatherwax, Rudd's son.

The road narrowed, and soon she was turning into a sandy car park above the cliffs. She bought a parking ticket, then checked her mobile. Perhaps Ken had left a message for her, and she hadn't heard the beep over the noise of the engine. But no, the screen was blank. She felt a wave of irritation at herself. She'd forgotten to charge it!

She replaced the phone in her bag, locked the car, and walked towards a red refreshments van parked by the entrance. She'd have a walk, and treat herself to a picnic on the beach before she went home.

"A cheese and tomato sandwich and a bottle of water, please."

"Sure, love." The van owner placed the items on the little shelf beneath the window. "Come out for some fresh air?" he asked chattily.

She smiled.

"I'm hoping to blow some cobwebs away," she said. "Pretty big ones, actually," she added.

"Well, you've chosen the right day for it." He smiled. "Wind's getting up." As he spoke, a gust caught at her, chilling her bare arms.

She collected her cardigan from the car, then made her way past a row of beach huts on the shallow cliff, and down a little wooden ladder on to the beach. Soon she was stepping on to a wide sweep of wet sand that rippled like the waves that had created it. Apart from a few people walking their dogs, she was alone.

Puddles of water left behind by the tide reflected the sky like big splodges of blue paint. She took off her shoes and stuffed her pop socks into her bag. The water would be cool, but at least she could have a paddle. She made her way to where the waves were breaking, the ridges hard and cool under her feet.

How the boys had loved to run about on the shore when they were little, she mused, chasing each other and building sandcastles. Sometimes their friends had come, too, and they'd all played cricket and football at low tide. What happy, busy days they had been.

THE sun went behind a cloud, and she shivered, pulling her cardigan closer. It was getting chilly. After her paddle, she'd have to find somewhere to shelter to eat her lunch.

As she walked, the argument she'd had with Ken that morning spun round and round in her mind. She'd chosen the topic of conversation carefully, hoping that it would be something that would draw them together again. She'd begun brightly.

"Where shall we go on holiday this year?" she'd asked.

"I don't think a break's going to be possible," Ken had replied curtly from behind his newspaper.

"But I've been looking forward to getting away." Despite her resolve, anger had surged up in her at his lack of interest. "I suppose you can't get

132

away from your precious business, is that it?" Immediately she'd uttered the words, she'd regretted them, but she was fired up now. "I'm so fed up with all the hours you spend at work!" she'd added.

"And I'm fed up with your lack of support," he'd snapped back, throwing his paper on the table. "Can't you see I'm doing my best to keep us afloat?" He'd headed for the door, only stopping to add, "By the way, I'll be working late tonight." Then the door had banged shut, and he'd gone.

"Oh, dear," Jenny muttered aloud as she recalled the scene, but she only got a squawk from a passing seagull in reply. She reached the sea and stopped, chill water pooling around her ankles. A frothy wave shushed and broke. How could they have drifted so far apart?

THE breeze that had been steadily growing sharper now snaked beneath her cardigan, reminding her that she needed somewhere to shelter. She looked towards the low ridge that edged the bay. That's where they used to have their picnics, there in the lee of the cliff. She'd always loved the sense of sea, sand and sky that seemed to envelop her there.

She was soon tucking herself in close against the cliff face. It was lovely and warm away from the wind. She took out her sandwich. One thing was clear, she told herself as she munched, things couldn't carry on as they were, for it was doing neither of them any good. She had to sort it out.

The sun felt warm on her face, and she closed her eyes. She always thought better with her eyes closed. She listened to the distant swish of the sea, and the screeching of the gulls. All else was silent.

She wasn't sure exactly what it was that made her open them again, but when she did, she found herself staring at a lone figure on the beach, walking along the edge of the sea.

The familiarity of his gait made her heart lurch. It was her Ken! Whatever was he doing here, she wondered? Was he clearing his mind, too? Her heart beat fast. Had he come because he'd had enough of her moodiness? Perhaps he was searching for the right words to tell her he was leaving her?

She stood up, and the movement must have caught his eye, for he turned towards her. For a moment, they stood there looking at each other. Then he waved and, with that affectionate gesture, all her anger and worried frustration melted away.

She began to run and, at the same time he did, too. It was like a cheesy scene from a film, she thought afterwards, though it didn't feel cheesy at the time, not at all.

They met in an embrace so full of love it took her breath away.

When eventually they sat down together, Ken placed his jacket around her shoulders.

"Can't have you catching your death," he said tenderly, pulling her close again. "What idiots we've been," he continued. "We've let our problems get between us. Do you remember how we always promised we wouldn't do that?"

Jenny nodded, immersed in the wonder of feeling close to her husband again.

"I tried your mobile," he added. "I wanted to say sorry."

"I forgot to charge it," she explained. "And it should be me apologising. I've been so bad tempered lately. I'm sorry. I really am."

"When I couldn't get you, I decided to come home," he said after he'd hugged her again. "I hate it when things are bad between us. The house was empty, so I dropped in to ask Pat if she'd seen you. She said you'd been round and were upset. I had a feeling I might find you here — at our special place," he added, smiling.

AS they began to talk, the floodgates opened, and all the tensions of the past few months poured out. Jenny told him about how useless she felt now that the boys had left home, and Ken replied by telling her how worried he'd been about the business.

"Why didn't you talk to me before?" she asked, snuggling close to him.

He bent to kiss the top of her head.

"You always seemed so preoccupied."

After that, they talked some more, but more importantly, they listened to each other, too. They'd each been so caught up with their own worries, they'd forgotten how to do that.

"I've had to let one of the lads go," was one of the things he told her sadly.

"And Natalie's moving away. When she leaves, I'm not going to replace her. We should just about scrape through this year then, I think."

"Natalie's leaving? How will you manage without her?" Jenny knew she was the mainstay of the office, and that her husband relied on her to keep things running smoothly.

Suddenly, she gasped.

"Why don't I help you out till the business gets on its feet again?" she asked. "I know I'm rusty, but I've been thinking of taking a computer course anyway, and I'm a good organiser. A quarter of a century of running a home and family gives you plenty of experience in that department!"

She looked up. Ken was smiling down at her, his eyes shining brightly.

"Really? I couldn't pay you anything, not to begin with anyway," he began.

"I wouldn't want paying," she remonstrated. "I'm your wife, remember?"

"Yes. You are," he murmured as he bent his head to press his lips to hers. "The best wife in the world." ∎

Dad's First Day
by Jan Clark.

BERTIE snuggled under his duvet.

"I like it when you read Peter Rabbit," he murmured sleepily. "I like it when he gets all wet in the watering can."

Alice closed the book and bent down to kiss him, loving the smell of just-bathed boy. She stroked his blond hair, so like his father Jack's.

"You'll be able to read it for yourself when you get to school. How long now?"

"Two more Sundays, then a Monday and I'll be there!"

"I bet you can't wait," Alice said.

There was a long, considering silence, until Bertie said, "I think I'm going to like it. Were you scared the first day, Granny?"

"I kissed my mum at the gate and went in with everyone else. It was the first time I'd ever been in the school. We didn't have lots of visits beforehand like you have nowadays. You just had to get on with it."

And that, she thought to herself was the way life seemed to be lived in those days – getting on with it, no fussing, making the best of things!

"But I loved every minute!" she added.

"Did Daddy like school?" Bertie loved hearing stories about his dad as a little boy.

Alice moved to the door.

"Well, not really at first . . ." she said cagily, and switched off the light.

"Why not?"

"I'll tell you all about it in the morning, love."

"Tell me now. Please, Gran, please?"

Bertie was adept at spinning out his bedtimes, but Alice wouldn't fall for this one.

Illustration by Ruth Blair.

135

"God bless, have a lovely sleep and nice dreams," she said firmly, and made her way downstairs.

Her grandson, about to start school! It seemed only a minute since he was born. And it seemed only a few months since his dad, Jack, started school. The troubles they'd had, though. Bertie would enjoy hearing the stories.

ALICE and Bertie sat in the sunny conservatory next morning and she started her tale. She described his father's voice from twenty-five years ago, shrill and stubborn, as she tried to reason with him on the first day of school.

"I don't want to go! I hate schools. I want to stay here with you and Sadie."

Sadie, their mongrel puppy, had recently been acquired from a rescue home.

"There isn't any choice, Jack, love. Children have to learn and school is the best place for that. You'll make lots of friends and know how to read and do sums and lots of other things," she finished lamely.

"I don't want to learn them and I don't need any friends now I've got Sadie." He pushed his bottom lip out. There had been a lot of that lately.

Alice was tempted to warn him about the wind changing.

She was almost in tears as she related the conversation to her husband, Ed, that night.

"I've done everything they say you should do: he's had two visits to look around the school, met Miss Carmichael, his teacher, who was lovely, but he's determined not to go. I couldn't wait at his age; I was desperate to do writing and learn songs."

"Me, too," Ed said, grinning. "But it wasn't for the classroom stuff; I wanted the proper football pitch and real goal posts. Jack's like me – mad on sport. He'll soon settle to that, I reckon, and the rest will come later."

Alice continued to stitch a name tag on Jack's grey trousers. The pile of school clothes sat there as a horrible reminder of tussles to come: shirt, tie, jersey, socks, and the blue T-shirt, shorts and gym shoes for PE. His black school shoes sat shining in the kitchen. At least, she thought proudly, she'd taught him to tie his laces.

She remembered his face, screwed up in concentration, as he mastered the tricky windings and bows, and the final triumphant grin when he managed it on his own. She had made him some gingerbread men as a reward.

"The first week is only mornings." She sighed. "How much trouble can he cause in three hours?"

Ed met her eyes, and both he and Alice pulled rueful faces.

"Plenty!" they said in unison.

Ed resorted to bribery in the end, after another week of stuck-out lips and sulks from their son.

"Tell you what; do well at school and I'll take you to the football on Saturday."

Jack's eyes lit up.

"Can I have a pie at half-time?"

Ed raised his eyes heavenwards.

"Only if you deserve it!" he warned.

WHEN Jack's first day arrived Alice could hardly believe it. Off marched her son, school bag in hand containing his PE kit, smart as paint in shiny shoes, his stripy school tie perfectly knotted as Ed had shown him.

She still felt guilty that they'd had to bribe him – it was against everything the parenting magazines told you – but since the promise of a football match all had been peaceful.

Jack hadn't shown enthusiasm – that would have been too much to hope for – but there had been no more talk of wanting to stay at home.

All that morning Alice couldn't settle. She did a little half-hearted housework and decided to take Sadie for a walk. Almost without thinking she made her way to the park, where the school field backed on to it. It was playtime and she could hear the shouts of children as they let off steam.

She peeked through the hedge and caught her breath – there was no sign of Jack! Several children in their smart new school clothes were running around, or clustered in groups, but she could see nothing of her son.

Horrid visions assailed her of Jack having to stand outside the headmaster's office, or being kept in disgrace on his own, or having to do jobs in the classroom as a punishment for bad behaviour.

She raced home, almost dragging poor Sadie along. But there had been no calls. She hung out her washing, did some much-needed weeding, changed out of her dog-walking clothes and prepared to set off and collect Jack, her heart in her mouth.

"Did you enjoy this morning?" she asked brightly as she set sausages and mash in front of him.

He grabbed his knife and fork and ate heartily, but stayed silent. After chocolate ice-cream he loosened up a little.

"I hated PE. The rest was all right, but I'm not doing PE ever again!"

Alice was taken aback. Jack loved sport, games and anything physical, just like Ed. He'd kicked a ball and practised throwing and catching ever since he could toddle. She might have understood if he'd set his face against poetry or singing.

She leaned forward and touched his hand.

"I thought you'd love PE; all that new kit to wear and a great big field to run around in."

Out came the bottom lip.

"Well, I'm never doing it any more and you can't make me." He scraped his bowl and stacked it on the draining board before flopping down on the rug with Sadie, ruffling her ears and squeaking her toy mouse.

"And neither can Miss Carmichael!" he finished fiercely.

Thinkstockphotos.

"CAN I have a word?" Alice asked the teacher next morning, feeling sorry for the poor woman, surrounded by infants waving coats, notes and pictures, clamouring for her attention.

Miss Carmichael waved the children into the playground and took Alice into a quiet corner.

"Your Jack was fine yesterday," she said, smiling, "and he's back today, so we must be doing something right."

"I don't like to fuss," Alice said, "but Jack came home saying he hated PE, and he's refusing to do it again. It's so unlike him that I wondered if anything went wrong. I didn't see him outside at playtime, either. Was he in trouble?" Her voice faltered as she faced the worst.

The young teacher reached out and patted Alice's arm.

"Jack did miss playtime, but he certainly wasn't in trouble! Ask him about it when he gets home!"

The school bell rang out and she went to meet her class in the playground.

"It was your fault – yours and Dad's!" Jack said later, picking at his fish fingers.

"My fault?" Alice was stunned.

"You shouldn't have taught me how to fasten my laces and do my tie."

Jack scooped up a forkful of peas and chewed away.

"Nobody else in the class knew how to do theirs; I was the only one. Miss Carmichael asked me to help the others so I did, and then I was late getting changed. I tied six lots of laces and five ties, and she did the rest."

Alice sat back in her chair, relief flooding through her. A lump came to her throat as she visualised Jack going along the line of classmates, tying ties and lacing shoes. It was a whole minute before she could trust herself to speak.

"Do you know what, Jack, love? Miss Carmichael's jolly lucky to have you in her class. I bet she was really pleased with you." She felt a little glow of pride, remembering the crash courses she and Ed had undertaken to make sure that two skills, at least, went with Jack to school.

Jack went a bit pink, doubtless remembering his teacher's praise.

"When's the next PE lesson?" Alice asked casually a few minutes later as

Autumn Is . . .

THE rapture on a small boy's face
As glossy conkers tumble down,
Spiderwebs like silver lace
String from branches russet-brown.
Purple daisies, tangy air,
Chrysanthemums so bitter sweet,
Little bonfires everywhere,
Crunchy leaves beneath one's feet.
Brilliant berries on the bough,
Varnished rose-hips all aglow
Like tiny scarlet lanterns now,
Where roses bloomed not long ago.
Spotted toadstools, red and white,
Squirrels laying in their store,
All this, beautiful and bright,
Autumn is, and so much more!

– Kathleen O'Farrell.

she pulled the foil from a couple of strawberry yogurts.

"Friday morning." He stirred the pot and scooped up some bits of fruit.

"I reckon Miss Carmichael would be lost without you to give her a hand again if she needs it," Alice said carefully. "It must be hard work looking after you all and making sure you learn well."

Out of the corner of her eye she saw Jack square his shoulders and set a firm expression on his face, as one who knows where his duty lies.

"I'll think about it," he said at last. "Sadie, playtime!"

He took a ragged tennis ball from the cupboard and trotted into the garden.

So your dad did really well in the end," she said, squeezing Bertie's hand.

"Did he go to PE after that?"

"He did, and he was in all the school teams, as well. The other children soon learned ties and shoelaces because the teacher told them to practise and gave a silver star to the ones who did it."

"Did Dad get a silver star even if he could already do it?" Bertie was very keen on strict fairness.

"Even better: a gold star and a big clap in assembly for being the most helpful boy in his class!"

"I haven't got laces," Bertie said, looking at his shoes.

They fastened with magic nylon strips, as did his trainers and slippers.

He gave a huge grin.

"But we have to wear a tie. Gran, when I get home I'll ask Dad to show me how to tie it." He suddenly looked worried. "Do you think he remembers how? I've never seen him in a tie. I don't think he's got one."

Alice thought for a moment. Jack had continued his love of sport into his work, and managed a substantial leisure centre where tracksuits were the dress code.

Alice hugged Bertie.

"I'm sure he does. After all, your grandad taught him. You'll be the smartest boy in the school!"

A Ribbon Of Blue

by Penelope Alexander.

THE curve of the path came into view, and Maisie was thankful she was nearing Crocombe House. This was not only because she knew Mrs Elston, the housekeeper, was waiting for her, but also because Cook might have saved a nice tea for all the maidservants.

Maisie hitched up her basket and rounded the corner, then came to an abrupt halt. There, on the path in front of her, lay a man, groaning.

Maisie's basket tipped, scattering fruit on to the grass. She was scrambling after the last rolling apple when black, level brows appeared above the coat-collar.

"Are you hurt?" Maisie called.

"It's my head," the owner of a very dirty face moaned, heaving himself against a tree trunk.

Maisie looked at the face, then looked again.

"Colm?" She gasped.

She couldn't believe her eyes. No-one from Crocombe had seen Colm for months. Maisie's knees shook, and she reached for the nearest tree trunk to steady herself.

Memories flooded back inside her mind – the smell of a hot meal being readied in Crocombe's kitchen last year, a doorway left open to welcome the cool breeze, and Colm Hayman, the footman, pushing past another bewildered servant, Walter, on his way out.

"Where do you think you're off to?" Lizzie Darch, one of the maids, had demanded.

Colm had drawn himself up.

"I've been dismissed!" he had said, his handsome face grim.

Chopping green herbs beside Lizzie, Maisie had gulped. Colm attracted trouble like iron filings to a magnet, but he was a good lad at heart, and

Illustration by David McAllister.

surely Mr Headon, the butler, would never turn anyone out so cruelly. Especially not Colm, who'd arrived at Crocombe barely grown, and owning nothing but his breeches and a torn waistcoat. Everyone was fond of him, despite his troublesome ways.

"Mrs Elston said I'm good only at causing accidents," Colm had said. "I'll not stay where I'm considered no use. I know I can do better for myself than this!"

"You mustn't leave without references!" Maisie had burst out desperately. "How will you live?"

"I'll find a way! I won't stay where I'm not wanted!" Colm had swept on through the kitchen and out into the yard.

Tearing off her apron, Maisie had run after him.

"Colm, come back! Don't do this!"

Colm had stopped and smiled, and looked at the crumpled apron she was twisting in her hands.

"You mind you don't lose your position over this, too, Maisie Chown!" he had said.

"But where will you go? What will you do?" Maisie's breath had caught on a sudden sob.

Working together at the big house, she had known Colm had no family to turn to. Luckily, being tall and presentable, he'd managed to find a place as a footman, but he had little to make him count in the hard world outside Crocombe.

"What will her ladyship say when she finds you've gone?" Maisie had asked.

"I doubt she'll notice," Colm had said bitterly. "You'd better forget me as well, little Maisie."

"I can't and I won't!" Maisie had said. Hot tears had burned her eyes and she'd lowered her head.

Colm, suddenly gentle, had done his best to brush them away before he'd reached for her hand.

"Think of me kindly, then. I swear I'll find you blue ribbons and dance with you at the next harvest supper!"

He'd kissed her fingers, winked, then strode across the yard and disappeared under an archway.

THE memory of that brave wink had comforted Maisie over the passing weeks. Colm had looked so determined; he'd surely survive – even do well in life!

Yet those at the house had heard nothing since his sudden and dramatic departure.

Seeing him now, months later, propped awkwardly against a tree like some muddy, ragged scarecrow, she could only feel anger towards the once-proud, handsome man who had brought himself down to the level of a common country tramp.

"You frightened the life out of me!" she said, getting up and shaking her skirts.

Colm managed a slow, painful smile.

"Yes, Maisie, that's me, in trouble as usual. And no, don't come over. I'll manage to stand by myself . . ."

Maisie ignored this advice. She put down her basket and hurried towards him.

"Thanks," he slurred, allowing her to support his weight. "Caught my head on those ash roots . . ."

Maisie looked at the great, damp knuckles of wood embedded in the path and then, with a shudder, the back of Colm's head.

"You've certainly taken a blow!" she said. She also noticed his coat was ragged, his trousers were filthy, and as for his boots . . . She bit her lips together to stop the tears.

"I'll guide you back to the kitchen," she said quickly, before dwelling further on Colm's condition. "You need some help. Cook will know what to do with you."

With an effort, she helped him loop his satchel on to his shoulder, and they struggled towards Crocombe.

"Sit there!" Maisie indicated a stool propped in the yard.

Wincing, Colm lowered himself and closed his eyes.

Maisie hurried into the kitchen.

"I need clean rags!" she told Lizzie.

The egg whisk in Lizzie's hand paused above the earthenware bowl.

At the same moment, Walter burst noisily in through the back door, shouting loudly to everyone in the kitchen and beyond that, believe it or believe it not, the Hayman lad was sitting in the yard, large as life and twice as natural, or he'd eat the billy goat's bonnet.

After that, it didn't take long for curiosity to drive Lizzie, Cook and everyone else from the kitchen into the yard to cluster curiously round the patient.

"Lean forward, please," Maisie said to Colm, ignoring the mild uproar they were causing as she bathed the wound on the back of his head as gently as she could.

Lizzie and Cook, clucking like hens, helped to tie the bandage around the patient's head. Colm gave his thanks, slid sideways off the stool and staggered a few steps to his left.

"You should lay up somewhere, my lad," Walter said. "Come on, here's my arm . . ."

"Make sure nobody sees!" Cook hissed. "We can't have ex-servants lolling in the stables or Mrs Elston might hear of it. And we all know what she'd have to say about it!"

Maisie watched the two men weave across the yard.

So, our handsome wayfarer has returned," Lizzie teased, exactly as Maisie had been afraid she would. "I can't think why on earth he would choose to turn pedlar to earn some money if not for your sake, Maisie Chown!"

"For my sake?" Maisie whispered, twisting a cloth over and over through her fingers. The shock of seeing Colm brought so low lingered still. "What do you mean?"

"Of course, for your sake!" Lizzie said impatiently. "Don't be coy with me, lady! Do you think I didn't see whose hand he kissed as he left all that while ago?"

"He never said he was going to tramp the lanes . . . poor Colm! What a terrible life!"

The girls walked back to the kitchen, for the work still had to be done.

Lizzie sighed at the innocence of her friend, while beating the eggs to a fine froth.

"Of course that's not what he said. But what else could he do, Maisie, being dismissed and without references, and him too proud to take his telling and come back to us?"

THAT evening, when they sat for supper, it was clear many of the servants knew the stables sheltered a wandering pedlar.

Maisie worried terribly in case some authority decided to throw Colm out a second time, and him having injured himself, too. Fortunately, Mr Headon was busy, and Mrs Elston – in any case, often kinder than her vinegary reputation allowed – didn't yet seem to realise who this particular pedlar was.

"Walter, I trust you to make sure there's no sign of the cheapjack by morning," the housekeeper said. "He must find somewhere else to complete his recovery . . . well, perhaps not until tomorrow.

"But I want everyone to understand we fail in our duty to the family if we encourage all comers to seek charity here. Word of things like this gets around fast."

* * * *

The tall windows shone black when Maisie pulled the curtains in the kitchen next morning. She quickly made a nourishing dish of bread and milk and covered it with a thick cloth.

Next she took a deep breath and pushed the door with a twist of her hip. Head down, heart pounding, expecting at any moment to be called to account, she scurried to the stables.

One of the horses stamped a hoof, and the smell of sweet hay drifted on the air.

"Watch out you're not in trouble for this yourself, my girl," Colm muttered, seizing the dish from her hand.

"I'm not going through all this to-do for nothing!" Maisie said. "I don't intend to get caught!"

But she was on edge all the same, fearing eyes in the walls and ears at every window.

Colm ate the food gratefully, wiping his mouth roughly on the back of his sleeve.

"Would you take this as payment?" he said, gulping a little.

Maisie, already hurrying to the door, peered doubtfully over one shoulder. Colm was shaking a wide ribbon free of his satchel. There was just enough light creeping under the door to see its colour.

"You know how I love the colour blue!" Maisie whispered, smiling at him

An Sgùrr of Eigg

IT is hard to imagine active volcanoes in Scotland these days, but 58 million years ago, the pitchstone lava that flowed from some of the last eruptions in the area gave rise to some spectacular features of the landscape that we know today.

The highest hill on the island of Eigg, An Sgùrr (the "notch") with its distinctive profile, is one of these. The two-hour climb to the top is popular with walkers, offering views from the summit of the whole island and its Hebridean neighbours. However, the view from the bottom is equally popular with the less energetic!

The peaceful scene hides a troubled past, as the island was the stage for some of the bloodiest episodes in the area's history, including plundering by Spanish mercenaries in 1588 and a series of reprisals resulting from the islanders' support for the losing side in the 1745 rebellion.

Following a series of changes of ownership, the island is now owned by the Isle of Eigg Heritage Trust, giving the islanders a real stake in their own futures, while the Scottish Wildlife Trust ensures the future of the island's natural heritage in its management of the site as a nature reserve.

in the thin light. As she accepted his gift, she said, "Colm, why don't you ask for your old job back? Everyone here wishes you would."

Her heart sinking, she watched him shake his head.

"I have my pride, Maisie. But look out for me, all the same . . ."

* * * *

Colm set up on the local green within a few weeks. When the housekeeper heard there were goods to be had, it was Maisie she dispatched to the little village.

Gone was the bedraggled traveller in mud-stained clothes, and in his place stood a well-set-up young man with curly hair and a wide smile.

Although his coat was still frayed, and his boots almost past repair, some of Colm's old confidence had returned. Maisie knew he'd seen her, but with several other pretty young women gathered around him, for the moment she thought he was pretending he hadn't.

"And what for Crocombe, miss? Silks? A thimble . . .?" he asked, turning at last towards her.

Maisie shook her head.

"Some of your best thread, please," she said demurely. "And Mrs Elston needs scissors."

Colm, with a wide grin, stopped pretending.

"I am glad to see you, Maisie Chown!"

Laughing, he swept a pretty box into his hands and opened it with a flourish.

It was brimful of shining blue. Maisie ruffled the ribbons, and they ran through her fingers like water.

"These are beautiful. They must sell well for weddings," she murmured without thinking.

"That they do," Colm agreed meaningfully. "I hope you still have the one I gave you?"

The look in his eyes made Maisie hope she wasn't blushing too much as she assured him she had.

"Her ladyship noticed you'd gone," she continued quickly. "I believe Mr Headon had some trouble from it. If you only asked, Lizzie says she's sure a job would be found again for you."

There was an embarrassed silence, making her wish she hadn't mentioned he'd remained the subject of kitchen gossip. She knew by now how proud he was. Colm, shrugging as if he didn't care, turned away to busy himself with other customers.

Maisie lingered nearby, and when he packed up, she pushed her own purchases into her bag and ran after him.

"Walter would put in a good word for you . . ."

"No-one willingly takes on a homeless pedlar such as I've become,

Maisie," Colm said. His eyes had darkened forbiddingly beneath those level brows.

He started walking again, forcing her to run alongside. Maisie caught at his sleeve, which tore with a sound like ripping goosegrass.

"That's the shoulder gone on my coat!" Colm said, skidding to an angry stop. "If you're going to be damaging my clothing, how am I supposed to keep tidy enough to impress anyone, let alone Mr Headon, for my old job back?"

Maisie halted, too, swiping away salt tears.

"Hear me out, Colm Hayman, and you might find there's someone in this world who cares enough about you to mend a split seam!"

His mood changing like quicksilver, Colm caught Maisie in his arms and held her close.

"I've missed you, little lass," he said, over and over, while they swayed together, his cheek warm against hers.

Two sparrows swooped and landed, chirping among the hazels.

"Don't cry! I came back, didn't I?"

"Let me mend your coat." Maisie sniffed, her head against his torn, rough sleeve.

She tilted her head to look him in the eye.

"And what will that cost me?" he asked, his voice gentle.

"A dance at harvest-time," she whispered. "I'm sure you'll be taken on for work, then – no questions asked."

And the trees beside the lane whispered as they kissed.

WEEKS later, after that evening when she'd sat on the kitchen steps at Crocombe and re-stitched his sleeve, Maisie thought constantly of Colm. Before he'd left, he'd said he might ask her to marry him.

"If you still find it in your heart to accept me when I return, wear my ribbon in your hair the next time you see me!" he said.

So Maisie counted the blue mornings and the clear evenings, and the leaves that turned slowly to red and brown and yellow beside the curving path. She found herself pleased to imagine all the hard work that lay ahead as the days moved on and summer ended.

For that was when Colm had promised to return.

✳   ✳   ✳   ✳

"A pedlar, you say?" Mrs Elston scandalised.

"Foreman's taken on many extras for the harvest," Walter explained. "Strong men are always needed to work the fields."

Maisie held her breath. Mrs Elston had a long, but particular, memory.

"Is he that great pedlar lad you told me about? The one with the knock on the head we sheltered a while back?" the housekeeper demanded of them. "He looked suspiciously like young Colm Hayman to me when I caught sight of him leaving." She turned sharply to where Maisie was wiping dishes. "And don't think I didn't see you crossing to the stables with food that morning, either, Maisie Chown!"

Maisie, surprised at how much was known about her movements, felt the silence in the kitchens stretch like the long road to market.

"We'd all struggle for food, being cast out as he was!" Walter dared to murmur into the silence. "That's why we've been helping the lad back into steadier work."

Thinkstockphotos.

"Walter gave him his old boots," Lizzie said. "I got him a shirt, and Maisie made him a neckerchief."

Mrs Elston turned her head away from them. She seemed to have something in her eye that took her a long time to dab clear.

"I never wanted the young lad to leave that day . . ." she said at last, her voice catching. "It was never my intention. It was all out of hand so quickly, what with tempers flaring – first Mr Headon, and then Colm, with me in the middle!

"The lad strode off before anyone could stop him. Luckily, it seems he has the sort of friends here we should all hope for."

Then, recollecting herself, Mrs Elston blew her nose and found she was urgently needed upstairs. She left Maisie, Walter and Lizzie staring at each other in amazement. Then, one by one, they began smiling.

"Well, I'll be blowed!" Walter said.

* * * *

After the relentless work of harvesting, Maisie's feet needed a rest. She had good reason to sit near the barn door, watching the comings and goings in the warm, moonlit evening.

She'd taken Colm his bread, cheese and ale at noon, so she knew he was

148

One Day

I'VE got a list called "One Day",
I add things every week,
Like one day I'll be slender,
My figure trim and sleek.
And one day I'll learn Spanish,
And French and German, too,
I'll learn to make a soufflé,
I'll study cordon bleu.
And one day I'll grow orchids
And learn the clarinet,
I'll write a brilliant novel,
I'll learn to fly a jet!
You're right, I know I'm dreaming,
For one day's far away,
Next time I make a list out
I'll label it "Today".

– *Maggie Ingall.*

nearby. But her favourite fiddle tune had been played three times at the harvest supper and still there'd been no sign of him.

"Maybe he's stopped in the lane. You know what those men are like for gossip!" Lizzie joked as she retied the shiny blue ribbon in her friend's pretty hair.

Maisie laughed, and quickly slipped away to try to find out what was holding Colm back from joining her and all his other friends at the long-awaited supper dance.

A harvest moon, huge, round and golden, lit the curved path and sent shadows looming deep into the hedgerows.

Colm's dark shape was tramping up and down beside the old ash trees like a restless giant.

"Whyever won't you come inside?" Maisie called.

"I'm not sure . . ." he called back.

"But you promised me a dance!" She ran up and tugged him forward into the bright moonlight. "Come on, hear that music!"

AS he raised his dark head to listen, Maisie realised he was now, more or less, the proud and handsome Colm she remembered.

He wore a light shirt, tidy trousers and a pair of worn but serviceable boots. New around his neck was the cloth she herself had painstakingly sewn for him.

"I look like an old scarecrow, Maisie," he said.

"Nonsense!" she said, firmly smoothing his shoulders. Then she threw back her head and looked him challengingly in the eye.

"I think you're frightened, that's all!"

Colm gripped her fingers tightly, as if he suddenly feared he might be slowly drowning.

"So what's supposed to be scaring me?"

He was cross and bewildered, she could tell, but she had no intention of apologising.

"You're afraid your friends will pity you as a cheapjack," Maisie said calmly, his ragged intake of breath telling her she had hit the nail on the head. "But I'm telling you now, Colm, nothing is farther from the truth! You have to believe that."

There was a long pause and Maisie trembled, fearing that she had gone too far.

Sounds of music and laughter from the dance floated back down the lane, and Maisie could hear Colm's laboured breathing as he considered what she had just said.

"You're right, Maisie," Colm said at last, lowering his head. "My mind's in a pickle of its own making, as usual."

"Now you listen to me, Colm Hayman," Maisie said. "Remember how Lizzie stitched you a new shirt, and Walter went and found you a pair of boots?

"Everyone likes to help where they can, but they'll always go the extra mile for someone they consider a friend – and they know just being sorry for yourself helps no-one."

For the first time since Maisie had known him, Colm looked ashamed of himself.

"I know what you say is true, Maisie Chown. I'm lucky to have them." He looked at her with the direct gaze she remembered so well. "But I never forgot my true friends, Maisie. I want you to believe that I never forgot any one of you."

MAISIE moved closer towards him, smiling into the warm welcome of his arms.

"Above all, I must make sure you'll never forget the girl who mended your torn coat and made you that neckerchief," she whispered, rearranging the cloth around his neck.

"Even though you haven't yet made any comment on the blue ribbon in her hair!"

He seemed to notice for the first time the ribbon he'd presented to her. His shoulders relaxed, and he reached up to touch her hair very gently, a look of wonder in his eyes. All of a sudden it was a very different Colm standing in front of her – a more confident man, sure of his feelings for this beautiful girl before him.

"You mean . . . I may ask to marry you?" he asked.

"If you don't, Walter says he'll eat the billy goat's bonnet!" Maisie said, laughing. "And goodness knows what Lizzie might do – let alone our Mrs Elston!"

Inside the warm barn, someone cheered and the fiddle-players restarted a lively jig. Colm caught Maisie's hand and together they hurried towards the dancing. ■

Black Beauty

"BLACK BEAUTY" is one of the best-selling books of all time, having sold approximately 50,000,000 copies. The author of the book, Anna Sewell, fell while walking home from school one day and injured both her ankles, causing her to be unable to walk or stand for any length of time for the rest of her life. She learned a deep respect for horses as a result of her subsequent dependence on them for transport.

The book was made into several film versions, the most recent and fifth of which was released in 1994, starring Alan Cumming as the voice of Black Beauty, with the horse Docs Keepin Time playing the title rôle. Docs Keepin Time had gone from an unsuccessful racing career to becoming one of Hollywood's leading equine performers. He also appeared in the successful "The Horse Whisperer", and has sired several offspring, some of which have gone on to have fruitful film careers of their own!

The Moviestore Collection Ltd.

Happy Memories

by Pat Posner.

PLEASE, Mum," Lily said when Hannah went into the bedroom to say goodnight. "Please let's have a Hallowe'en party this year." Hannah sat down on the edge of the bed and gazed at her daughter. Hallowe'en was over two months off yet, but she knew why Lily had mentioned it now.

Before her dad died, this was the time when the three of them had made their first visit of the year to Pumpkin Patch Farm to carve messages and pictures on pumpkins.

"I know I was only six when we had the last party," Lily continued quickly, "but I can remember the fun we had getting the barn ready for it, going to the pumpkin farm and Farmer Stuart helping us choose the pumpkins." She took a deep breath then launched in again.

"We went most Saturdays for weeks before Hallowe'en to see how much our pumpkins had grown. Then a day or two before the party, Farmer Stuart brought the pumpkins here in his noisy old truck."

A picture of Tony and the old farmer struggling to lift an enormous pumpkin off the back of the truck sprang instantly to Hannah's mind and she could almost hear the laughter of that day again.

Lily was still wandering down Memory Lane.

"I remember how great it was when the day of the party arrived," she said. "How much everyone enjoyed it. I can remember things from way before I was six, too. Like when I was a baby and you put my pram under a star mobile, and how Dad gave me a lick of his toffee apple. He used to love Hallowe'en so much."

Hannah nodded. Tony had come up with the idea of holding a party in their huge old barn the first year they were married. It had been so successful he'd decided to make it an annual event. But if it hadn't been for his legendary parties, Tony wouldn't have gone to town that day to buy Hallowe'en props, and wouldn't have been involved in that accident . . .

Of course, that year's party had been cancelled. Then, for Lily's sake, on the next two Hallowe'ens, Hannah had made brooms and the two of them had dressed up as witches and gone "flying" round the village in the dark. But she knew Lily had thought it a poor replacement for the barn party.

Since being knee-high to a butterfly – Hannah felt the familiar tug of sadness as she recalled that favourite description of Tony's – Lily had got involved in decorating the barn, making scary masks, thinking up games.

"I think," Lily said, fiddling with her duvet, "Dad would be upset if he knew we'd stopped having the barn party. We should do it to remember him, like . . . like we wear poppies on Remembrance Day."

She raised her head and met Hannah's gaze.

Illustration by Richard Eraut.

153

"And . . . and, I really miss packing a picnic and going to look at the pumpkins, getting the barn ready, decorating it and . . . and everything."

Seeing the longing in Lily's eyes, Hannah realised that she'd been thoughtless – or rather, too busy thinking of her own feelings. Of course Lily missed doing all that. And she was right about her dad as well. He wouldn't have wanted them to stop having the Hallowe'en party.

"All right." Hannah pulled the girl close for a hug. "I'm working tomorrow but we'll go to Pumpkin Patch Farm on Saturday and choose some pumpkins. And on Sunday we'll make a start on the barn. It'll need a good tidy-up and clean-out, and maybe a coat of whitewash, too. I'll ask Nicola to bring Drew and Lucas over one day and they can all help. But there's plenty of time to do that."

"Only ten weeks," Lily said. "Then Hallowe'en will be here."

THAT'S lovely news, Hannah." Nicola glanced up from packing a jar of strawberry jam to smile at her best friend. The two of them had worked part-time at Pam's Pickles and Preserves, a small cottage industry in their village, for three years, but they'd been friends ever since coming to live here as new brides. Their children were friends, too.

"Are you sure about it, though?" Nicola continued. "I know all festivals and anniversaries must be hard for you, but Hallowe'en . . ."

Hannah nodded.

"Hallowe'en was the one Tony liked best. More than Christmas, even. Maybe it was because of his parents having all the family for Christmas so, apart from us having our own tree, everything else happened at their house."

"And Hallowe'en happened at yours," Nicola said.

Hannah guessed what Nicola was thinking. She'd once told her friend that if it hadn't been for Hallowe'en, Tony would still be alive.

"Having the party again will be the right thing for Lily, Nic," she said. "And who knows?" She sealed a package with a firm touch. "It might be just the right thing for me, too."

"It's probably time you started socialising a bit," Nicola said. "Tony wouldn't have wanted you to become a recluse."

"I'm hardly that. Sometimes, what with taxiing Lily to and from swimming, horse-riding and after-school club, I feel like I'm never in the house."

"Yes, but that's Lily socialising, not you."

"I see you, Pam and the others three mornings a week," Hannah protested, "and a couple of afternoons, too, if there are extra orders. And I help out at the church bring 'n' buys, and have days out with the in-laws, and visit my sister and my parents . . ."

"OK." Nicola grinned. "So you're not a recluse. You just don't leave the village much."

154

"That's about to change." Hannah willed her voice not to waver. "Tomorrow I'm packing a picnic and taking Lily to Pumpkin Patch Farm."

ATURDAY dawned with a drift of clouds dancing across a sunlit sky. When Hannah went into the garden to pick plums for the picnic hamper, the dew was heavy on the grass and the scent of damp hedges and blossom drifted in the warming air.

A perfect day for our outing, Hannah thought as she went back indoors.

Lily chattered excitedly as they packed bread rolls stuffed with salad, chicken legs, cheese, plums – and the selection of crisps and snack bars she "couldn't live without".

An hour later, with the village left way behind, they were driving through deeper countryside. Still chattering happily, Lily gazed out the car window.

"Whatever it is that's growing in these fields is the same golden brown as your hair, Mum."

"It's wheat," Hannah replied. "The ones on the opposite side, with the poppies dancing around, are cornfields. If we have our picnic near a cornfield you might be able to hear the corn whispering."

Hannah pulled in at the next lay-by. There wasn't much traffic around, and as they sat eating, sure enough they heard the rustle of the ripening corn.

"This is nice," Lily said after a while. "The food, the corn, the scent of flowers. But," she added, "I can't wait to get to the farm and choose our pumpkins."

"Hint taken." Hannah smiled, and began packing up the remains of the picnic.

"I wonder if Farmer Stuart will remember us?" Lily said as she helped.

"It's changed a lot since we were here last." Hannah parked the car and glanced across at the fields. "Looks like they've made a corn maze."

"The Pumpkin Patch sign is over there." Lily pointed. "So there'll still be pumpkins, Mum. Won't there?" she added anxiously.

"Sure to be," Hannah said, crossing her fingers.

They needn't have worried. Round behind the farmhouse, the sight of pumpkins growing proudly on tangles of vines greeted them.

A tall, dark-haired man with a rugged, outdoorsy face came towards them, taking long strides on the wooden planks that formed a pathway between the pumpkins.

"Can I help you?" he asked.

"We're here to choose pumpkins for Hallowe'en," Lily said before Hannah had time to speak. "And to carve names and pictures on them."

"You've come at the right time," the man said. "The pumpkins are a month old – their skins are perfect for carving on."

"We used to come when I was little," Lily told him. "But we haven't been for a while. Farmer Stuart might remember us, though, because he used to show us good pumpkins to write on and he was always here when we came to see how big our pumpkins were growing. Is he here today?"

Hannah held her breath as she waited for the reply. Farmer Stuart hadn't exactly been young . . .

Maybe her anxiety showed in her face because the man smiled at her before replying to Lily.

"Farmer Stuart's my dad. I'm Rob. My wife and I took over the farm around three years ago when the work was getting a bit too much for him."

Lily sighed and looked disappointed.

"Dad . . . Farmer Stuart still helps out on special occasions, though," Rob said. "And I guess that's what this is if you haven't been for a while. Hang on here and I'll go and fetch him."

"He's nice, isn't he, Mum?" Lily said as Rob hurried away, and Hannah nodded. His kindness to Lily, as though he'd realised how important this visit was to her, had warmed her heart.

"I'm glad Farmer Stuart's still here, though," Lily added.

Before long, they saw Rob and his father approaching. The elderly farmer was hobbling a bit, but apart from that, Hannah thought, he looked the same as he had the last time she'd seen him.

Lily ran towards the two men. Hannah couldn't hear exactly what her daughter was saying, but she guessed she was telling Farmer Stuart her name and asking if he remembered her. He was smiling and nodding, replying to Lily in a rumbly voice. Then he patted his arm, Lily linked her hand through it, and they began to walk slowly down the path.

Rob came on ahead. He smiled when he reached Hannah.

"Dad remembers when you used to come every year," he said. The smile left his face when he added, "I'm sorry to hear about Lily's dad; she told us this is the first time you've been back here since he died."

Once again, Hannah felt a depth of understanding in this man. It's what he leaves unsaid, really, she thought.

"We're here, Mum."

Hannah turned to see Lily beaming and the elderly farmer holding his hand out.

"Good to see you again, Hannah," he said. "I'm sorry to hear about Tony. Glad you're continuing the tradition he started, though. I'm going to help young Lily here choose pumpkins and do the carvings. Perhaps you and Rob would like to get lost," he finished on a chuckle, and Lily giggled.

"He means in the new corn maze, Mum," she said. "I might go in the maze next time we come. Today's just for pumpkins."

Hannah glanced doubtfully at Rob.

"I don't want to keep you from your work," she said.

"Ah, but showing off the maze is a huge part of my work now. It isn't quite how I want it yet; this year is a sort of practice run. I'll redesign it and, hopefully,

156

Llanberis, Dolbadarn Castle

BUILT by the Welsh prince Llywelyn ap Iorwerth (Llewelyn the Great) in about 1230, Dolbadarn Castle guards the base of the Llanberis Pass, the main route through Snowdonia's majestic mountains to Anglesey, the stronghold of the Gwynedd princes.

The imposing ruin inspired J.M.W. Turner's magnificent 1802 landscape and continues to impress today. Visitors might recognise the area as one of the locations used in the film "Carry On Up The Khyber" where it stood in for the Khyber Pass and parts of the Himalayas!

next year it will indeed be a maze to get lost in. Come on, let's leave these two to the pumpkins."

MAYBE I should have brought Lily back before this," Hannah said to Rob as they made their way to the maze, set in a huge cornfield. The outer walls of corn were taller than Rob and the inner pathways seemed to stretch for miles.

"I just didn't realise how much it all meant to her," she went on. "And it's so good of you and your dad, making her so welcome."

"It can't have been easy for you coming here again," Rob said.

"Not as hard as I thought it would be," Hannah replied thoughtfully.

Talking easily, they meandered into the maze.

"Tony would have loved this," Hannah said. "Hallowe'en was his favourite time so he'd have been visualising a Hallowe'en event at night with everyone carrying a torch to light up ghosts and witches hiding among the corn."

"That's a terrific idea," Rob said. "Maybe I'll try that next year if I can get the maze the way I want it."

Every now and then he stopped and, drawing lines and curves in the air, tried to explain what he wanted to do to improve things.

"It's too easy to find the way out right now."

In spite of that claim, they did actually lose their way for a few minutes. Then they spent a few more minutes recovering from their laughter.

As she finally walked out of the maze, Hannah realised it had done her good. It had made her see it was time to find her way in life again.

When they rejoined Lily and Farmer Stuart, Hannah could see her daughter was happier than she'd been for a long time, too. She was bubbling with excitement and pride as she pointed out the pumpkins Farmer Stuart had helped her choose.

"Some will grow very big," Lily said, "and one will grow absolutely ginormous. I've carved some special words on that one. I don't think you'll be able to see anything today but when we come back the pumpkins will have grown a bit bigger and so will the carved letters and pictures.

Early November

THE morning the storm was gone
The fields thin with water,
The branches waving bare,
Their last leaves curling the sky.

And there in a land left gaunt,
Novembered by days of wild –
Swans, some folded against the wind,
Some flying at half mast above.

The huge slowness of their grace in the air
In the tangled wool of the sky;
Their beauty bigger in the buffeted air,
Their whiteness whiter.

They were ice carvings
Held and frozen high;
Hope of a new year still sleeping
In the land so sore below.

– Kenneth Steven.

"You can look at most of them next time we come, but you must promise not to look at my special one till I say."

"I promise." Hannah nodded and drew a cross over her heart.

"And now, sweetie, we'd better go."

She stepped over to Farmer Stuart and hugged him impulsively.

"Thank you so much for today," she said quietly. "You, too, Rob," she added.

"We'll be back soon," Lily said as she waved goodbye.

THE weeks seemed to fly past. It took most of September to get the barn cleaned and whitewashed and they only managed two visits to check on the pumpkins.

Now, though, they were on their way to the farm again.

"It's so good that we're going today," Lily said. "Halloween's in three weeks and we need to check the pumpkins to make sure the pictures and messages are still showing up properly. If they are, Farmer Stuart will cut the pumpkins and leave them to cure before he delivers them. I wonder if Rob will be there today?"

They had only seen him to wave to last time.

Farmer Stuart was standing looking at the pumpkin patch when they arrived.

"It's just as well you've come today," he said. "They're ready for cutting. How about I show you how to do it, Lily?"

"Will that be OK, Mum? Oh, here's Rob," she said.

"I'm glad you're here," she told him. "I was hoping you would be. You can take Mum out of the way while I cut pumpkins with Farmer Stuart. You could go in the maze again."

Rob smiled at Hannah.

"I've just finished taking a couple of families through," he said, "but I'll take you if you really want to try it again."

Hannah laughed.

"You've already taken me round it twice. I've a feeling 'yes' would be the wrong answer."

"I'd rather show you some ideas I've sketched out for next year instead. I think I've come up with a good design for a Hallowe'en maze."

I THINK it'll be great," Hannah said as, sitting at a large table in the farmhouse kitchen, she pored over the plans Rob had sketched out. "I'll bring Lily and my friend's two lads to try it out," she added, wondering why he was so quiet.

"You know I told you my wife and I took over the farm three years ago?" he said suddenly. "Well, what I didn't tell you was that she – Chloe – only stayed a few weeks before she realised neither I nor the farm was what she wanted."

"Oh, I see. So that's why you seemed to understand how Lily and I felt the first time you met us," Hannah said. "You've lost someone you loved, too."

She couldn't help but wonder how Chloe could have left someone as kind, gentle and caring as Rob. Knowing he was married, she had never let her thoughts dwell on him, but even so, she had had the sense of a connection between them.

"She's remarried now and living in Birmingham. It isn't Chloe herself I miss – more what might have been. What maybe still could be with the right person," he added. "That's the reason I didn't tell you I was divorced, Hannah. I thought if you knew I was free, you might also guess . . ." He broke off and stared helplessly at her.

"Guess what, Rob?" she asked softly.

"The first time we met I felt pretty sure you could be someone special to me," he said. "The second time, I was absolutely sure. But I didn't know if you were ready for anyone new to come into your life. I still don't know. I just know I don't want to wait until the next year's maze is ready before seeing you again."

Hannah looked into his face and a warm glow flowed through her.

"I don't think I want to wait that long, either."

"We'll wait until after your party," Rob said. "That's for you and Lily, your family and friends. After that . . ."

"Mmm," Hannah agreed. "After that . . ." She knew she didn't have to say any more.

"You can look at what I carved on the ginormous one now," Lily said when Hannah and Rob returned to the pumpkin patch. "Farmer Stuart says it's the best one ever."

"Indeed it is," he agreed gruffly.

Hannah felt a lump in her throat when she saw the words *Happy Memories* etched large and clear on the pumpkin. They would never forget Tony, but she knew he would have wanted her and Lily to move on and start making new memories. And it seemed right that it had all come about at his favourite time of the year.

She smiled at Rob and knew he was thinking the same. ■

Here Come The Girls!

by Lorna Howarth.

"**O**H!" As Odelia rustled her newspaper shut and snapped it down on the dining-table, her sisters, Charity and Drusilla, looked up from their boiled eggs and gazed at her in astonishment.

They rarely spoke to each other before breakfast was finished and their young housemaid had cleared away the crocks.

The three sisters were alike in looks, with large grey eyes and straight brows. They dressed similarly, too, in pale high-necked blouses and long

Illustration by Len Thurston.

161

dark skirts. Only their hair marked them out as different. Charity wore her dark hair loosely bound, while Drusilla's was swept up in no-nonsense fashion on the crown of her head. Odelia, prematurely greying, wore her fading locks drawn back into a bun at the nape of her neck.

They were sitting in the breakfast-room, where they spent the majority of their time together. It was a comfortable room, with horse-hair upholstered chairs, a warm, cosy hearth, and red velvet curtains. It seemed even more inviting this morning as a grey November fog bumped thickly against the latticed windows.

W**HATEVER** is the matter?" Drusilla demanded, while Charity continued to stare, a triangle of buttered toast suspended halfway to her mouth.

"A hundred and nineteen suffragettes arrested in London!" Odelia announced, flushing and jutting out her chin as she always did when she was cross. "And some of them have been hurt. How dreadful to think of such brave women being jostled in that way."

"What did they do? They must have been arrested for something," Drusilla responded, reaching for the teapot. Hers was always the calm, sensible voice in any discussion.

"A delegation tried to gain entrance to the House of Commons."

"But why?" Charity asked, frowning.

"Because the Conciliation Bill that would have given some women the vote isn't going to be allowed any more parliamentary time, that's why," Odelia replied, her voice rising. "I really can't help but sympathise with Mrs Pankhurst. Oh, dear," she added, "I do hope they're being treated with civility."

"You talk as if you wish you were one of them, sister," Drusilla put in.

"Sometimes I do wish that, Drusilla," Odelia retorted sharply. "Perhaps if there were a WSPU group here in Martinswold . . ." Her sentence lay unfinished between them.

"What exactly is the WSPU?"

"Really, Charity, sometimes your head is like a sieve," Odelia admonished her. "I've told you before, it stands for the Women's Social and Political Union. The WSPU are militants."

"Oh, yes, the 'Millies', of course."

"If we lived a little nearer London instead of here on the east coast, for two hat-pins I'd join in one of their marches." Odelia stood up, raising herself to her full five feet six inches, and glared at them defiantly. Her sisters stared back, wide-eyed.

"Oh, dear. Then you could end up in prison, too!" Charity fingered her pearl necklace nervously. "Whatever would Father have said to hear such a thing?" she whispered.

At the mention of their father, silence descended on them.

Odelia pushed her chair aside, sighing deeply. Why was it that all matters affecting their lives seemed to come back to their father?

Though he'd been an authoritarian, she'd loved him very much, and after their mother died had been proud to run the home for him and her younger sisters.

As the years passed, however, he had become very particular and strict in his ways, and she had begun to feel confined. Even now, two years after his death, she felt they were still living in his shadow.

"I wish I'd been born a man!" she exclaimed suddenly, aware that she sounded more like a petulant child than a mature woman. "Then I could be a politician or a lawyer, and do something useful. It really is all so very unfair!"

Drusilla stared at her.

"Women's suffrage may be a noble cause," she commented drily, "but it seems to be bringing a lot of trouble with it."

Odelia glared at her.

"Change shouldn't be resisted just because it's uncomfortable," she remonstrated. "The whole world is changing, sister! Just think of all the steam locomotives and motor cars there are now. Why, we even have a new king in dear George the Fifth. And attitudes must change, too," she said firmly.

FOR the remainder of the day, the thick fog pressed down on the village, trapping the smells of cooking and chimney smoke. It seemed to press down on Odelia's spirits, too, and she felt hemmed in and restless after her outburst at breakfast.

After writing up the household accounts, she decided she would brave the weather to stretch her legs. She could deliver the pot of Charity's raspberry preserve that had been promised to the vicarage, and give in their weekly contribution to the Poor Fund at the same time.

In the hall, Odelia leaned close to the coat-stand mirror to pin her hat in place, glancing at the grey strands in her hair, then down at her dull skirt and jacket. She pulled a face at her reflection. She felt as drab and colourless as the clouds of November fog that waited for her outside. And just about as useless, too.

They were fortunate that their father had provided so well for them, she knew that, but sometimes she found herself envying the women who had to work for a living. They had something she did not: purpose.

Some suffragettes were dressing in the green, white and purple of the WSPU. How wonderful it would be to wear such colours, she thought, as she turned towards the street door. How liberating.

Their father had never allowed them to wear bright shades. They were too vulgar, he'd said.

She made her way up the steep cobbled street towards the top of the hill, going slowly to avoid bumping into people in the fog, and allowing her thoughts free rein. She half-wished she hadn't read about the demonstration. It had unsettled her, and now she had a headache beginning.

T HE headache stayed with her throughout the day, and by the time evening came, she was glad to draw the curtains and sit down. As she eased herself back against the cushions in her favourite armchair by the fire, her mind returned to the subject that had been nagging at her all day. If only she could turn her back on their father's teachings and decide things for herself. But how did one undo so many years of meek obedience? How could she begin to break the habit of behaving exactly as her father expected?

She looked across the room to where her sisters were happily occupied, Charity absorbed in a book of Mrs Beeton's recipes and Drusilla sorting out her pretty embroidery silks. Both of them looked quiet and contented and entirely at peace.

She sighed. She was being silly. What did the three of them need with emancipation, after all? They were quite happy as they were.

Weren't they?

Odelia reached out to pick up her newspaper, and again she felt restless as her interest stirred. The suffrage movement was gaining momentum, and it felt as if it were pulling her with it.

She let the paper fall on to her lap, leaned her head against the wing of the armchair and closed her eyes, imagining herself part of the march. Yes, there she was, her hat bobbing gaily above the rest. She was wearing a white blouse with a green skirt, and a coat of . . . goodness, she hardly dared think it. Purple!

She imagined herself striding along in front of the group, holding aloft a banner. It held the WSPU's motto. *Deeds, Not Words!* it proclaimed.

She felt herself relax, the flickering fire warming her. How marvellous to fight for better opportunities for women.

She was listening to herself shouting, "Votes for Women! Votes for Women!" when suddenly she sat upright, opening her eyes wide. All at once, everything was clear! She was the one who had been putting obstacles in her way, no-one else!

A cinder rustled as it fell through the grating to the gathering ash beneath. If Mrs Pankhurst and her daughters could take up the mantle, there was absolutely no reason why she couldn't, too.

As she reached for her writing tablet, she began to feel as if she were floating. It was as if a weight had been lifted from her.

She glanced up at the sepia photograph on the mantelpiece and met her

Armagh

AN ancient royal centre of Iron Age Ulster, Armagh (from *Ard Macha* – the hill of Macha) has been settled since ancient times. Its influence has been felt throughout the whole island for over 6,500 years. Nearby Navan Fort, now a National Trust centre, tells the story of those early inhabitants for today's visitors. The atmospheric surroundings bring to life those ancient days recorded in the myths of the Ulster cycle, when Connaught's Queen Mebh led the famous "Táin Bó Cúailnge" (cattle raid of Cooley), opposed by Ulster hero Cú Chulainn, the Hound of Ulster, then barely out of boyhood.

A major ecclesiastical centre since the mid-400s when St Patrick founded his church, Armagh now boasts two cathedrals dedicated to the saint, which watch over this elegant town with its Georgian architecture surrounded by the beautiful Ulster scenery.

father's dark, forbidding stare squarely and purposefully.

"I'm sorry, Papa," she said silently, "but I have to follow my own path."

Her heart beating fast, she snatched up her pen. She had a very important letter to write!

DURING the night, the fog that had ensnared the village began to clear, and by the following morning the sun was shining brightly again.

The important letter that Odelia had penned was soon safely in the postal service collection box at the top of the hill.

Each day after that, she trawled through the daily newspaper with even more attention than usual, and when the eagerly awaited reply to

her letter came, she opened the envelope with trembling fingers, clasping its contents to her in delight when she had read them.

In the weeks that followed, she began to jot down notes, and Drusilla and Charity often saw her mysteriously writing in a little notebook she had taken to carrying everywhere with her.

* * * *

Two days before Christmas-tide, Odelia awoke with a flutter of excitement in her stomach. The gloomy November weather had given way to a fine December, and the day was a crisp, clear one, with smoke drifting calmly up from frosted rooftops into a clear forget-me-not sky.

When they had breakfasted, she donned her coat and a new hat which she had daringly trimmed with bright green, white and purple ribbons.

"Green for hope, white for purity, and violet for dignity," she'd told Drusilla and Charity as they watched her stitch the ribbons into place. "And G – W – V also stand for Give Women Votes! Isn't that clever?"

Now she lifted her hand to give the ribbons a final pat, then opened the front door of Ivy House and turned up the winding hill which led towards the

Days Indoors

WINTER spreads its snowy mantle,
Puffs its icy breath with pride,
But behind our curtained windows
We are warm and safe inside.

Cones and logs are in the basket,
Toasted crumpets for our tea,
Magazines and books are waiting,
Many favourites on TV.

Freezing days indoors we snuggle,
Sunny ones we walk awhile,
Then with tingling toes and faces
We return home with a smile.

Rainy days are made for hobbies,
Music waiting to be played,
So when winter brings its challenge
We can face it unafraid.

– Chrissy Greenslade.

village green.

"Come along, sisters," Odelia called over her shoulder as Charity and Drusilla hurried to catch her up, a wooden crate knocking between them. "We don't want to be late, do we?"

With heads held high, the three sisters made their way up the hill, their determined strides attracting stares as they went.

Odelia's heart was full. She had expected her sisters to be embarrassed or ashamed when she'd told them of her intentions, but they had surprised and touched her with their wholehearted support.

"We women must stick together," Drusilla had said proudly.

At the church, they turned right and made their way on to a large area of grassland bordered on one side by the churchyard and a row of sturdy oaks on the other.

It was market day on the green. Several brightly coloured stalls were set out along the path, and a steady straggle of folk were already going about their business.

Odelia led the way to a spot a little way back from the path and motioned Drusilla and Charity to set down the crate. She tested it for steadiness then stepped on to it.

AS she set her foot upon the solid wooden structure, she hesitated for just a moment. What had possessed her? What would her father say if he could see her? But then she raised her chin.

Her father had been a strong, principled character, and surely it was that very strength and conviction that was running in her blood now and urging her to do this?

In spite of his stern ways in his later years, she had the feeling that he would have approved of her integrity in standing up for a principle that she believed in so strongly.

She felt as if her whole life had been leading to this moment. At a quick nod of approval from her two sisters, she took a deep breath.

"Friends!" she called. "I am here to talk to you about a matter of great importance." A few heads turned.

"Women's suffrage!"

One by one they came to listen: mothers with children at their skirts, housewives with baskets over their arms, old women clutching their shawls about them.

There was a scattering of old men, too, puffing at their pipes, and even some passing roundsmen stopped for a few moments.

"Why should women not have the vote?" Odelia asked them all.

At first, the words came stiltedly, for she had never spoken in public before. But, as her confidence began to grow, they became filled with the passion she felt in her heart.

THE path was soon full to overflowing. There was some lively banter, of course, especially from the men, but she answered all their questions and comments vigorously and with the strength and conviction of her beliefs.

She wasn't naive enough to think everyone would agree with her message, but at least they were there and they were listening.

"Now," Odelia declared as she neared the end of her prepared speech, "I am delighted to announce that the Women's Social and Political Union is forming a group here in Martinswold – and I am to lead it," she added proudly.

"Any of you who are interested in furthering the cause are very welcome to attend. The first meeting will be held in the village hall next Friday, six-thirty prompt."

She finished to applause, and was not at all concerned to hear a few jeers, too, for she had expected that.

Charity clapped her hands with the others.

"Oh, well done, sister!" she said, helping her down from the box. "I never knew you had it in you to be an orator. That was wonderful!"

Odelia's heart was full. At last, she had found a purpose – to fight for women's rights. It was a cause she believed in with all her heart, and she knew she had the passion and commitment to inspire others to fight for her cause, as well.

We will get the vote in the end, she thought, I'm certain of it. And who knows what might follow on from that? True equality of the sexes? Was that even possible? The very thought made her giddy.

Not in her lifetime, perhaps, she admitted realistically. But it would come one day, she was sure of it. If she and her sisterhood kept on fighting for the cause so dear to their hearts! ∎

Not Just For Christmas

by Sue Cunningham.

MARGIE switched on the tree lights and bent to warm her hands on the radiator. It was bitterly cold; too cold for snow, she would have said, but the white flakes already starting to drift past the window were doing their best to prove her wrong.

She moved across to draw the heavy curtains and the pink rubber mouse on the window-sill caught her eye. She sighed to herself – she'd thought she'd removed every reminder of Buttons. The familiar cat basket and all his well-worn toys were still tucked away in the cupboard under the stairs, though – after sixteen years of companionship she couldn't bring herself to throw them into the rubbish bin just yet.

Buttons had been a Christmas present in the days long before it was deemed unacceptable to introduce a new pet into the house at this time of year.

Margie smiled fondly as she remembered how her son, Steven, and his children had arrived

Illustration by L. Antico.

169

unexpectedly on Christmas Eve, the tiny kitten tucked tightly into Steven's overcoat. The little ones were still full of excitement over the pantomime they'd seen that afternoon and had already decided on a name for the kitten – Buttons, after their favourite character in the matinée performance of Cinderella.

"See, Gran! He's got some black spots on his white front. They look just like buttons, don't they?"

"They do indeed." Margie had lifted the sleepy kitten up to have a closer look. "He's lovely, isn't he? I'll have to find something comfortable for him to sleep in."

"It's all right, Gran," the youngest one said importantly. "Daddy's bought everything you need. We've even brought him a toy to play with."

The pink rubber mouse had been produced from a paper bag and placed in the new basket alongside the sleeping kitten.

And Buttons had been home.

SIXTEEN years ago. It seemed like yesterday. Margie collected the old rubber toy from the window-sill now, marvelling that it had lasted so long. She put it to one side, planning to tidy it away with the other things later.

The house seemed so empty without Buttons in it that she'd even delayed her homecoming today with extra Christmas shopping she didn't really need. Never mind. Steven and the family were all coming for lunch tomorrow and the little house would be full of noise and laughter; and she'd be kept busy enough this evening with all the last-minute preparations and wrapping of gifts.

The children were all grown up now, and there was even a new great-grandchild to keep her occupied, but as she pulled the roll of Christmas paper from her shopping bag, she found herself recalling how Buttons had always liked to "help" with the gift wrapping – white paws darting at the coloured paper and twitching tail tangled in the festive ribbon as he rolled over and over waiting to be tickled.

Margie smiled sadly at the memory. The wrapping would take less than half the time this year.

Perhaps she should think about getting another cat. Steven had already tried to persuade her, but she couldn't imagine replacing Buttons.

"I'll take you down to the cat rescue centre this weekend, Mum," he'd said. "You can pick out another kitten."

Margie shook her head.

"I can't be doing with a new kitten at my age. Maybe I might think about getting an older cat, but we would have to wait until after Christmas, anyway. You know these organisations don't like you taking a new pet home at this time of year. Not just for Christmas, and all that business. They're scared people will abandon them when Christmas is over."

Steven smiled.

"I don't think anyone could ever accuse you of that, Mum. Well, if you don't want to think about it right away, why don't you ask Emma next door to keep an eye out in case something suitable comes her way? That wouldn't hurt, surely?"

Emma was Margie's young neighbour, a veterinary nurse who volunteered at the cat rescue centre in her spare time.

Margie pursed her lips.

"I'll think about it."

SHE finished her last-minute wrapping now and settled down in front of the television to watch an old black and white film. This was the hardest time of day, the time when Buttons used to creep into her lap, grumbling with pleasure as she stroked the top of his head.

Her lap felt odd without the warm weight of the cat. Feeling foolish, she pulled a heavy cushion on to her knees, resting her hands on top of that instead.

* * * *

She must have nodded off because she was awakened by the doorbell. James Stewart was still on the screen so she couldn't have been asleep for too long. Margie looked at her watch; it was just gone nine. She tipped the cushion on to the sofa and went to the door.

The shape on the other side of the glass was too small to be Steven so she flipped on the porch light. You never could be too careful these days.

It was just young Emma from next door, pink cheeked and wrapped up for the seasonal weather in a striped woollen scarf. Relieved, Margie opened the front door to invite her in.

Emma smiled.

"Sorry to bother you so late, Margie, but I saw your tree lights were on and knew you must be home. I wanted to ask you a favour."

Margie was curious.

"Oh, yes?"

Emma bent to retrieve something from the porch. It was a cat basket with a tiny black kitten inside.

"Tell me if I'm out of order," she began, "but I know you lost Buttons earlier this week. I wondered if you might help us out with this little fellow. He was brought in a fortnight ago. We've been hand-rearing him ever since. We need someone really special to take him on."

"You've been talking to Steven, haven't you?"

Emma nodded, looking sheepish.

"You'd better come inside, love." Margie peered into the cat basket; the kitten was wide awake, tiny pink mouth wide open in complaint. Her face softened. "I really wasn't planning on getting another kitten, Emma."

Against her better judgement, though, she unlatched the basket and reached inside.

"Now, let's have a little look at you," she murmured, lifting the kitten against her chest. He was almost completely black apart from two white socks on his back legs.

"The girls at the rescue centre have been calling him Boots. Puss in Boots, you know." Emma gave her a conspiratorial smile. "I thought of you straight away, Margie. Buttons and Puss in Boots – I wondered if it was some kind of lucky omen. Maybe it's fate."

"Or maybe it's just a coincidence," Margie said briskly. She placed the kitten on the floor, watching as he staggered across the carpet on unsteady legs, stalking towards the discarded pink rubber mouse.

Margie became aware of Emma watching her thoughtfully.

"He's due a feed shortly – you know how they need their routine when they're little. If you're not keen on the idea of taking him I'd better get him home. We've managed to wean him off the bottle now but he still needs lots of care. The centre isn't fully staffed over Christmas so I said I'd bring him home with me, but I'm due to visit my parents tomorrow . . ." Emma trailed off hopefully.

MARGIE was torn. The kitten was curled up now on the rug next to the rubber mouse. Not a bit like Buttons – the old cat had always favoured the warm spot under the radiator.

He was such a little kitten, but his spirit was obvious and, although she didn't want to admit it, very endearing.

Margie cleared her throat.

"Well, it seems a shame to move him now he's settled," she said gruffly. "Perhaps it would be best if I do keep him – just for a few days, mind, as a favour to you. I wouldn't do it for anyone else, you know, not at this time of year . . ."

Emma looked relieved.

"That would be great. You really would be doing me a huge favour."

"Anyway, it would only be temporary, wouldn't it?" Margie added, looking down at the sleeping kitten. "I'm sure the centre wouldn't approve of you rehoming him permanently, today of all days. I know the rules. Not just for Christmas, and all that."

"You're absolutely right," Emma agreed, closing the door behind her as she stepped out into the frosty night.

"But just sometimes," she whispered to herself, swinging the empty basket with a secret smile as she hurried down the path, "rules are made to be broken. Merry Christmas, Margie." ■

Gentle Ben

TELLING the story of a young boy who manages to convince his father to allow him to keep an orphaned bear cub as a pet, Gentle Ben was based on a children's novel first published in 1965, set in Alaska, and ran from 1967 until 1969.

Gentle Ben himself was played by both Bruno the trained bear, who weighed a whopping 650 pounds at his peak, and by British actor Patrick Newell in a bear suit. Patrick's rôle in the show is little known about, and he's considerably more famous for his rôle as "Mother", the spymaster in "The Avengers".

Clint Howard played the young boy. Clint did well as a child actor, but struggled as an adult, unlike his brother Ron, who starred in "Happy Days" and went on to become a famous movie director.

In 1969, the cast of the show released an album of tracks they'd recorded together, called "The Bear Facts", which included the track "I Love To Eat" sung by the man who voiced Gentle Ben in the show!

174